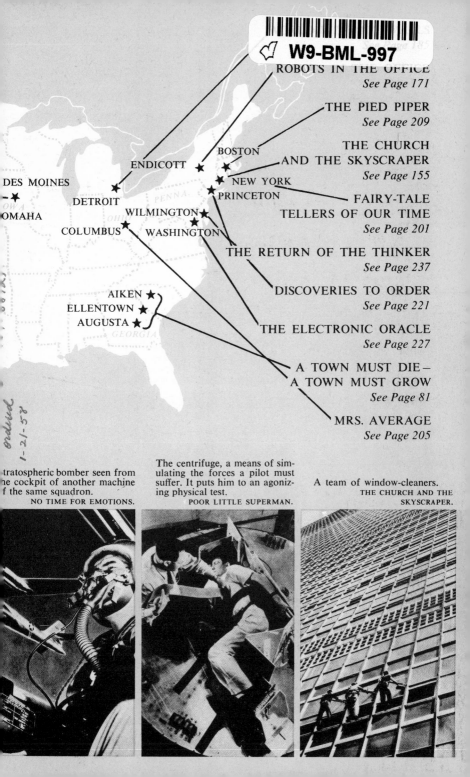

BOSTON
ENDICOTT
NEW YORK
PRINCETON
DES MOINES
DETROIT
WILMINGTON
OMAHA
COLUMBUS
WASHINGTON
IOWA
PENNA.
OHIO

AIKEN
ELLENTOWN
AUGUSTA
GEORGIA

Ordered
1-21-58

tratospheric bomber seen from
he cockpit of another machine
f the same squadron.
NO TIME FOR EMOTIONS.

The centrifuge, a means of sim-
ulating the forces a pilot must
suffer. It puts him to an agoniz-
ing physical test.
POOR LITTLE SUPERMAN.

A team of window-cleaners.
THE CHURCH AND THE
SKYSCRAPER.

Tomorrow
Is Already Here

BY

ROBERT JUNGK

TRANSLATED BY MARGUERITE WALDMAN
WITH AN INTRODUCTION BY HERBERT AGAR

Simon and Schuster
New York, 1954

Library of Congress Catalog Card Number: 54–6672
Dewey Decimal Classification Number: 973.9

MANUFACTURED IN THE UNITED STATES OF AMERICA
BY H. WOLFF BOOK MFG. CO., INC., N. Y.

CONTENTS

CONTENTS

INTRODUCTION

THE AUTHOR *of this book has lived a life symbolic of our times. He was nineteen, a Jewish student in Berlin, when Hitler came to power. His father was a writer. His friends and relatives felt strong in their old-fashioned German liberalism.*

The day after the Reichstag *fire, Robert Jungk was arrested for anti-Nazi activities. Released (because of good fortune and good friends), he went to Paris to study at the Sorbonne. Two years later, although deprived of his German nationality and of all status, he returned to the* Reich *illegally to work for a subversive press service. Within fourteen months he had to flee again, this time to Czechoslovakia, where he founded another anti-Nazi agency. When Prague fell in 1939, he transferred his activities to Paris. When Paris fell in 1940, he transferred them to Switzerland.*

Here again he was arrested and jailed, in 1943, because his anti-Nazi writings were too strong for neutral nerves. He was soon released through the good offices of a powerful American friend, and in 1944 and 1945 he was Central European correspondent for the London Observer. *Meanwhile, he completed his much-disturbed education, taking his degree at Zurich with a thesis on the resistance of the Swiss press to the censorship of Metternich.*

In 1945 he was back in Germany—East as well as West. In 1946 he spent three months in the United States; then he returned to eastern Europe to report for the Swiss press on Yugoslavia and Hungary. In September, 1947 he came back to America as correspondent for the same Swiss papers. Here he remained, except for a few months, until 1953. Readers who wonder how the author had access to so many semisecret places in our country should remember this long resistance to tyranny—which was well known

*to the authorities. They should also remember that a superb jour-
nalist, accustomed to discouragement but not to defeat, can get
into the most unlikely places.*

*We should not be surprised that the author, after such a life ex-
perience, is sensitive to any symptom of inhumanity and "sniffs the
approach of tyranny on every tainted breeze." The picture he presents of the United States may seem dismally pessimistic to anyone
less alert for the first signs of trouble; yet the book is of high importance for two reasons. First, it is not solely our own country
which is herein portrayed and lamented. The author is attacking
a deformity of the whole Western world—the materialism which,
if continued, must dehumanize us. The effort to explain life in terms
of the inanimate, the rage to bend every time-honored institution
into the service of the new metallic demons, the eagerness to turn
even the humanities into an imitation of natural science (an eagerness which began in Germany, not in America)—this is the great
modern heresy. And like most heresies, it is in fact a wild exaggeration of an otherwise sensible point of view.*

*Hating this heresy, the author seeks to describe it in its purest
form. No patriot should object to the choice of the United States
as an example; for these horrors exist in our country, as they exist
through our threatened world. And since the United States is very
large and very zestful, her vices and her virtues appear in jumbo
size, easy to isolate, easy to describe. The author, however, is little
concerned with anybody's virtues in this book. He is hunting down
a deep persuasive vice. And "for love of grace" let no European
assume that he is absolved from the guilt. On both sides of the
Atlantic, we are all in some part citizens of this degenerate "tomorrow."*

*The second reason for the book's great merit is that although
it is written in anger it is also written in compassion, and in the
hope that man may still find his way home from the cheerless, air-
less, moon world into which the applied sciences have enticed him.
The author knows that until we become finally demoralized we must
continue to puzzle over why we are here, over our relation to eternity. And this ancient, healthy question may restore us to sanity.*

Even if we get to the moon quite literally, we may still while away the long nights in the space ship by dreaming of

> *Children for memory: the Faith for pride.*
> *Good land to leave: and young love satisfied.*

The author also knows that many of our simple pieties and dignities have not yet succumbed to his infernal "tomorrow." He knows that they may repossess our hearts at any moment. This gives his book an overtone of hopefulness which could scarcely be derived from his reported facts.

Nevertheless, I would like to add a note of warning to any reader who has not recently traveled throughout the country and who may therefore be tempted to believe that some parts of it truly resemble this grim "tomorrow." Such a "tomorrow" is doubtless possible. And indeed it is "already here," in the sense that the facts reported in this book are true. But so far, thank heaven, these facts are all entangled with happier aspects of our past and present—and thus they are ameliorated.

The author may fairly select, for his own purpose, such details of American life as he chooses to discuss; but we must not assume that an accurate report upon these details constitutes a portrait of our nation as a whole. In fact, it is always a mistake to generalize about America, which contains so many climates, races, economic and regional interests, and such varied ways of life, that many millions of Americans must slip through any net of generalization. (The author, incidentally, does not often generalize. It is the reader who must be warned against this temptation.)

Finally, the author at one place seems to minimize the unpleasantness of what he is describing. In dealing with remote Los Alamos, he tells us about the visitor's trouble in getting in, but he says less about the resident's trouble in getting out. Yet when I was in Los Alamos my friends complained sadly of their isolation from the great world of science which they had once inhabited. They said that the West could lose its leadership in atomic research if this isolation continues.

"How am I to know," said one professor, "whether I have wasted

the last two years? Perhaps a colleague in England or in France has been doing exactly my work. Perhaps the questions I am studying have been already answered. In the old days we could help and serve each other at every stage, and on every problem—but no longer."

This is a warning, and an example of a suicidal quality in our "tomorrow." And it is "already here."

HERBERT AGAR

PART ONE

Grasping at Omnipotence

"We claim that since 1917 Russia and America have been converging upon technical omnipotence, that they have been thereby diverging from Western Europe."

ADRIEN TUREL

THE BOUNDLESS EMPIRE

WHEN Christopher Columbus undertook to seek the shortest sea route to India for his Queen, he knew so little about the region for which he was embarking that he accidentally found a "New World." The x-millionth visitor who travels to America today in the wake of the great seafarer tends to take with him rather too much than too little information concerning his destination. For nearly every one of us has felt the influence of Americanism in some form or other before ever setting foot on American soil. For us all, in the course of recent years, Uncle Sam has been transformed from a distant relative into a near neighbor, an almost daily visitor with whose home, customs and habits we believe ourselves to be better acquainted through an abundance of magazines, books, pictures and films, than many a country geographically nearer at hand.

Even so, Columbus's lot may well fall to the best-informed modern traveler. He comes to an utterly different country from what he had supposed. Behind the picture of the new world familiar from a distance he discovers another, highly singular one, which appears to him strange and dangerous.

Only under protest does the visitor gradually admit to his mind impressions which run counter to his expectations. At first he wishes to dispose of them as exceptions, set them aside as transitory phenomena. But slowly it dawns upon him that the sum of all these "appearances" may represent a new and singular reality,

3

an entirely different America still in the process of taking shape.

Certainly the outward signs do not reveal much of this other America. They are fair and freshly cleaned. The Statue of Liberty stands welcoming at the entrance to New York harbor with a promise of tolerance and humanity. The skyscrapers beckon in rows of gleaming windows and duly radiate optimism. Nowhere are the symbols of a freedom-loving democracy, proud of its origins, hidden or impugned. On the contrary: precisely because from year to year they are losing their real influence and strength, they are given a more conspicuous place in the show windows. But in fact, "the log-cabin President," "the rugged individualist," "the self-made man who worked his way from rags to riches"— have scarcely more connection with the actual present of the United States than cathedrals, castles, cancan and folk music have with the postwar realities of Europe. They have become museum pieces, attractions for tourists and grateful topics for speakers at a loss for ideas on patriotic occasions.

For the United States, too, despite outward appearances, has changed profoundly in the past two decades—at least as profoundly as the European countries convulsed by inner and outer upheaval. Something is breaking through the façade of the new world which I should like to refer to as the *newest world:* an America no longer in agreement with the guiding principles of its previous history and presenting, ever more plainly, features of a totalitarian nature.

In order to come in contact with this newest world one must leave the urban centers and ride out into the suburbs where the working world overlaps the living world, and individual human existence increasingly fits itself into the uniform of standardization. The centers of these groups are no longer the church, the school or the town hall, but the centers of production and consumption, the factory and the "supermarket."

But the newest world is seen most clearly after one has bidden farewell to the metropolitan civilization of the East and Middle West and turned to the once rural or entirely unsettled area of the South, Southwest and West; for that is where the evidences of the other America have been multiplying since the beginning of the Second World War with the rapidity of a gold-mining town.

Here are the great armament factories with their brand-new mass migrations, the metallic shimmer of oil refineries and mechanized network of chemical industries. Here, above all, are the military reserves, the laboratory towns, the testing grounds. Not only geographically are they segregated: politically, too, they lead a life apart. The rights of freedom have been largely suspended in them, and experiments are attempted with every form of administration from open dictatorship through enlightened absolutism to outright socialism.

One who has had contact with these forthright manifestations of the newest world will recognize them also where they have not yet emerged with such distinctness. For all that is uniform, standardized, inhuman in its exclusive striving toward efficiency, is still today so interwoven with the democratic, Christian and humanitarian pattern of the "good old days" that it is not immediately discernible.

There is a reason for this. Whereas in other countries totalitarianism erupted with revolutionary violence and then set to work immediately to wipe out the traces of a freedom-loving past, the process in the United States is taking an evolutionary form. Therefore we find an interplay of the old and the new, of the remains of freedom and the beginnings of slavery, which indicate that the final decision has yet to be reached. Even those few who are deliberately working toward a new tyranny opposed to the American tradition are clever enough to make use of the phraseology of freedom.

For this trend in the United States there are, of course, various illuminating and relevant political explanations. But such an approach is not within the scope of the present book. Here an attempt will be made to portray and explain the disquieting development in another way. For it arises, in my view, from a process reaching far beyond the internal or external political orientations of the moment.

Looked at historically, the tendency away from freedom seems to spring from the same source which yesterday and the day before watered the tree of American liberty; that is, the constant striving to open up new domains, the constant pressure toward new boundaries. The frontier, which in the course of a century and a half was pushed from the Atlantic to the Pacific, has deeply influenced America's thinking, her spiritual climate, and, not least, her domestic economy during the nineteenth century. It symbolized the country's unconfined spirit of progress, it was the cause of the perpetual stresses due to the finding of new riches. At the frontier there were no rules, none of the impediments of civilization. It was the paradise of the pioneer, the land of "unlimited possibilities," in which every man of sufficient strength and spirit could stake out a claim upon the future.

But by about 1890 the pioneers had conquered and occupied the entire territory of their own nation. The dynamic energy of the frontiersman had to seek new goals which could lie only beyond the sea or in the great tracts of land to the north or south.

It might at that time have been possible for the pressure toward new frontiers to have transformed itself into "pure imperialism." But the voices which prophesied an imperial destiny for the United States and tried to point the way to adventures in colonial conquest gained little hearing. After the short and not very popular war with Spain the adolescent power preferred to turn to other than territorial conquest. It sought, under the guidance of science and technology, for frontiers not to be found on maps: frontiers open to anyone who attacked them with energy and dared to cross them.

While other powers quarreled over provinces, islands, tracts of wilderness, thereby ruining each other, America went to work to develop her factories and laboratories. The new pioneers were enterprising financiers, scientists and engineers. These fertile minds did not need to be persuaded. If they were not already in the country they came willingly to the United States, attracted by the vast resources and potentialities for development which they found nowhere else in the world.

Thus the United States in the course of half a century developed into the foremost scientific and technical power. Her new frontiers lay and still lie mainly in her own laboratories and workshops. The apparent broadening of territorial boundaries in the last few years through the establishment of a world-wide net of military bases is indubitably defensive in scope. This widespread defense belt is intended primarily to serve a vastly more far-reaching and ambitious strategy, daily and hourly being carried on in the experimental centers of the homeland.

For the Americans today are concerned with bigger things than land ownership. They are fundamentally more ambitious than even their sharpest adversaries believe. Their efforts do not aspire to the mastery of continents, still less to that of the entire globe, but to higher things far than these. America is striving to win power over the sum total of things, complete and absolute mastery of nature in all its aspects.

This bid for power is not directed against any nation, class or race. It assails no particular way of government but the ways of creation, which have scarcely fluctuated within the memory of man. Clouds and wind, plant and beast, the boundless heavens themselves are to be subjugated. The stake is higher than dictators' seats and presidential chairs. The stake is the throne of God. To occupy God's place, to repeat his deeds, to re-create and organize a man-made cosmos according to man-made laws of reason, foresight and efficiency: that is America's ultimate objective. Toward this her chief efforts are directed.

This is a revolution as convinced of its successful outcome as any other revolutionary movement. It is furthered by statesmen, applauded by the masses, encouraged by the police. For it promises all riches, it proposes to take nothing from anyone. It destroys whatever is primitive, whatever grows in disordered profusion or evolves through patient mutation. What it cannot observe and measure it subdues indirectly to its power. It says the unsayable. It knows no awe.

The slaves employed by the Grasp at Omnipotence are not foreign nations but the elements themselves. Each year, it has been calculated, this army of "slave energies" increases by millions of "horsepower" and "heat units." Nothing is left untouched, nothing unexplored. Even the inmost core of heaven and of matter must be utilized—the sources of life and of the soul. There is no pause for death, no respect for time. Present, past, future are jugglers' balls to be tossed about. How tame an amateur was Prometheus compared with his distant American disciples!

It was long assumed that this reaching for omnipotence could remain without influence upon America's religious, moral and political character. But as elsewhere, and in some respects more strikingly, with the rise of the applied sciences and technology, the pillars of democracy, Christianity and personal ethics in the United States have begun to totter. Where formerly belief and conscience were the sole criterion, the names of the new judges are *purpose* and *results*. To these the only valid question is: "What is it good for?" All and everything, the smallest and the largest, must now be submitted to the test of utility.

Even man, the actual inventor and director of this purpose-bound world, has in the end been unable to keep himself free of the new bondage. Because of the happiness it promises, the American pays the highest possible price for this grasp at omnipotence —his freedom as a God-made person. His individual impotence is the price of a share in the omnipotence. The frontier of our time imposes on those who seek it a condition unknown to the pioneers who preceded them: subordination to collective effort and discipline.

In those days, each man could set out on his own, with company of his choosing, his firearms, a team of horses or oxen and a covered wagon full of provisions, into the unknown distance which promised wealth. The still unexploited soil was waiting for him, harvests and money rewarded his efforts with tangible satisfactions.

How different are the new pioneers! Their laboratories, workshops, testing grounds are not their own. They themselves are conceivable only as the vanguard of a gigantic industrial army. Behind the construction and launching of each rocket, each splitting of an atom, each chemical experiment, each working of an electronic brain, stands a highly developed technical apparatus, an enormous sum of sacrifices in time, strength, money and individual liberty. Only in his financial, organizational and personal relationship to the hierarchy of the joint enterprise is the pioneer of today conceivable.

It naturally follows that the new pioneer himself is subject to the application of the same methods he applies to the conquest of nature. He, too, is scientifically observed, tested for his capacities, made use of down to his smallest ability and, like any other tool, discarded as soon as he ceases to fulfill the required purpose. The "free will" must in this connection be flatly classed as an unstable element and ruled out—man, the uncertain factor, must be replaced by as reliable a type as possible. As in every revolution, the rebels, the Prometheans, the discontented must disappear. The reliable, tractable, average man becomes the new ideal pioneer.

Thus in the United States there is now in formation a world such as there has never been before. It is a man-designed, pre-arranged, highly controlled and continually "improved" creation. It has its own kind of beauty and terror. For although the human creators have taken pains to ban fate, chance, catastrophe, misfortune and death from their creation, the banished ones return all the more insistently: errors of calculation by the statistical planners, failures of technical equipment, accidents and explosions bring an accumulation of disaster.

Even the old dark myths of the veiled picture whose draperies no one may lift, of ghosts, demons, regions of witchery, even of hell itself, take on fresh valuations in this so precisely calculated, so rationally founded world. For the average man moves about in this test-tube world, this secondary nature, quite as uncertainly as did his forebears in primitive nature, because only the specialists—and often not even they—understand the things and powers they have brought into being.

This newest world is no far Utopia, no fable of the year 1984 or of a still more distant century. We are not, as in the novels of Wells, Huxley and Orwell, safely separated by the broad moat of time from that overcoming, ravenous future. The new, the different and the frightening is already among us. And so—as history shows—has it ever been. The morrow is already present in today, but harmlessly masked still, hidden and disguised behind the familiar. The future is no fantasy cleanly distinguished from actual life: the future has already begun. But it still can, if recognized in time, be changed.

In this newest world, infused by the future, the distinction between day and night, between light and darkness, has lost its validity. The act of the first biblical day of creation is annulled by this latest resurrection of Prometheus. That the modern process of production shall not suffer interruption the artificial suns of electrical projectors burn from sundown to sunrise. In nearly all the big cities of America may be found emporiums and drugstores which announce "We never close." It will be only a short step to the moment when the "northern lights effect" already being developed in a California laboratory will tear the nightdress from heaven forever.

And so it goes with each single act of creation described in holy writ. Man produces artificial matter, he builds his own heavenly bodies and prepares to release them into the firmament. He creates new species of plants and animals, he places his own mechanical beings, robots fitted with superhuman perception, in the world.

There is just one thing he cannot do. It is not given him to cry, in the words of the Bible, "And behold! It was very good." He may never relax his hands in his lap and say that his creation is completed. Restlessness and discontent remain with him. "For behind each door we open lies a passage with many other doors which again we must unlock, only to find, behind each, others to still others," a chemical research worker—one of the creators of artificial worlds—once remarked to me.

It seems as though the import of all this creation were no more than further creation. Production calls for ever more production, each discovery for further discoveries to serve as a protection against the consequences of the preceding one. Man no longer finds leisure in which to enjoy the world. He consumes himself in fear and worry about it. No sense of joy and no hosanna accompany the new act of creation.

This dissatisfaction with the man-made newest world, often so strongly felt in the United States as to find vent in fearful and destructive imaginings, seems to me one of the most hopeful signs for her future. Pessimism about civilization is no longer the fashionable pose of a small circle of artists and intellectuals, but the general expression of a deep and critical concern.

To be sure, such doubt still exists side by side in the same breast with the old spirit of boundless, wanton activity, of daring much and hoping all. But the shriller the *happiness* propaganda becomes, the more self-satisfied the smile of satisfaction over the "highest standard of living in the world," the more disturbing grow the doubts.

There are many who seek relief in "amusement," in sexuality, alcohol or neurosis—the so-called escapists. There are others who resign themselves, and some few who battle consciously against the trend forward into totalitarian, technicalized mass existence. Attempts are being made to humanize labor, to fit the machine to human psychology, to decentralize the swollen conglomerations.

But at present all this has a quality of play-acting or of deliberate cult. The great spiritual change, which would have to express itself in the recognition once again of human limits and the rediscovery of moderation, is not yet apparent. Help for this lies neither in messianic preaching nor in impatience. The transformation can indeed come only from bitter experience. Only when the convulsive grasp at omnipotence finally relaxes, when the *hubris* dissolves and gives place to humility—only then will America be recovered by Him Whom it has discarded, by God.

PART TWO

Grasping at Heaven

BIRTHMARK OF THE NEW ERA

Alamogordo, New Mexico

No ONE got out at Alamogordo. It must be the rain, I thought. It almost never rains in New Mexico, and when for once the heavens open up everybody who can stays at home. A poor day, therefore, to ask your way to an object of interest not on the map. The half-frozen Indian squaw standing in the luggage room, blue with cold, had no idea what I was talking about, and the stationmaster was equally nonplused. The waitress in the Café Plaza had at least heard of the "big hole." But she advised me to keep away from it. A certain Pancho Gonzales had grazed his sheep there against the regulation, had fallen asleep and a couple of weeks later had been admitted to the county hospital. "He got too much radictivity," she said as she served the scrambled eggs. An ill-shaven man at the next table looked up from his newspaper. "Radioactivity, Alice. . . ." She replied, somewhat piqued, "So what?"

The man with the newspaper was right when he advised me not to visit the place without a permit from the military authorities. I realized this an hour later as I stood before a high fence and read a yellow sign. This said in red letters in English and Spanish, "Danger. No admittance." I had traveled a few thousand miles to see the crater birthmark of a new era made by the explosion of the first atom bomb. I was standing before grilles and *no admittance* signs. This was the new era, all right. No mistaking it.

So back into gray, wet, drowsy Alamogordo to seek advice from the editor of the local paper. That is nearly always the best place to go if you wish to find your way in an American city. The hospitality,

15

sincerity and helpfulness of American newspaper people know no bounds. They date from the "good old days" when there were no security measures and no fear of spies. And so I found it here. My confrere, Morgan, wearing a broad-brimmed hat, was in his office, which smelled of chili peppers and printer's ink, accepting advertisements over the telephone as I entered. To visit the crater wouldn't be so easy, he opined between two calls. As a matter of fact, it wasn't quite settled which military department had the say. Holloman Air Force Base occasionally flew visitors over the crater, but they couldn't go there on foot or by car. That was for decision by the Santa Fe office of the Atomic Energy Commission. It had jurisdiction over the "big hole" and its immediate vicinity. But now the Guided Missile Center in El Paso also wanted a say because it was experimenting with long-range missiles in the surrounding desert, and a rocket might go astray. "It's a war to the death between the services, friend," he said. "It wouldn't surprise me if a little bomb went off one day. After all, what's the stuff there for?"

Yes, he remarked later when he had slipped away from his office for half an hour, one had pictured the thing differently in 1945. When the town councilors of Alamogordo heard the big explosion of July sixteenth hailed on the radio as "the beginning of a new era for humanity," they had immediately ordered the erection of a national monument. Alamogordo was to become a tourist center, and Mr. Cakkins, a down-and-out metal digger who had incredulously watched the rising of "the big sun" from his mountain cabin early one morning, hoped at last to draw dividends, as guide, from an inexhaustible vein of gold, the tourists. "Well, that's all washed up. You know why," resumed Morgan and then plunged at once into the thick of the paper war between the departments to get me a permit to inspect the "big radioactive hole."

The permit took its time. My letter of introduction from the State Department was not enough. They had sent back to Washington for inquiries. There, presumably, my dossier was being perused, telegraphs were ticking out the particulars. Examined, re-examined, the re-examination examined again, and all that because someone desires to look at a hole in the ground in a bit of wilderness!

That is the reverse side of the Promethean urge. That is the shadow of anxiety which follows the foolhardy; these are the weights of caution and mistrust round the ankles of those who storm heaven.

But I had no need to be bored while I waited. There is scarcely another region of North America where Indian antiquity, embroidered with legend, is so alive as in this part of New Mexico. Here the most ancient cave settlements of the country have been found, here are the loam huts and the curious jumbled citadel of the Pueblo Indians. "America's first skyscraper," the travel agency leaflets call it. I spent some time with Miss Kuhrtz, a social worker of the United Pueblos Agency, visiting the settlements under her care.

"These are the remains of the age of giants," she remarked as we came, on our way from one village to another, upon dead volcanoes, weirdly shaped rocks and high four-cornered plateaus. Once, according to Indian tradition, all other creatures were gigantic, only men were small. Winged beasts crouched over abysses, dragons and snakes lurked in caverns, gigantic and armored monsters lay in wait for men, women and children. But the "twin gods" came to the rescue. They climbed to the "black Mesa," challenged Tsebayo, the most malevolent of the giants, to a duel and killed him by a stratagem. They allowed themselves to be swallowed and, as soon as they had slid down the mighty gullet, pierced his stomach from the inside with their stone spears. In his collapse the giant is said to have shattered entire mountains. He finally expired, vomiting smoke and fire about him, and his bloodstream hardened into black lava.

One perhaps even better acquainted with the Indian sagas was the Catholic Father K., a missionary of Bavarian origin whom Nurse Kuhrtz took me to call on. He lives in one Pueblo of Isleta, not far from Alamogordo. We were sitting in his cell when I complained of finding all this secretiveness about the Alamogordo crater silly. "Certainly," he said, "to us whites it's something new and unusual. But to my Indian parishioners it seems as a matter of course that a people has holy places which only a few chosen persons may ap-

proach. The Pueblo Indians have always had such forbidden places
and have them to this day. And they ask me ironically, but with
serious faces, why the white man needs to protect his holy places
with so many watchmen, high-tension wires and alarm systems.
'With us the law of the ancients is enough,' they say. . . . 'Fences
are put up for cattle who don't understand words, or to keep out
wild animals. Men know how to respect secrets.' "

"How does he know all that?" I asked the social worker as we
left Isleta. She did not reply at once. Then she said dryly, "Because
he eavesdrops on the Indians. Because he records the conversations
they carry on in a special dialect for the initiated with a hidden
microphone. He, too, is only a white and can't respect secrets. . . ."

There was still no word from Washington, and by this time I
knew all four corners of Alamogordo as well as if it had been the
waiting room of a court. The sun had returned and was burning
hotly. The little park in front of the county hall faded to a dusty
gray. Over the "Cradle of the Atomic Age and of Rocket
Development" (as one reads on entering the town) lay an atmosphere of disappointment and listlessness.

Even my helpful newspaper colleague, Morgan, was out of humor. He was caught between rival factions who accused each
other in the town council and at public meetings of sabotaging
Alamogordo's future. A group of younger citizens demanded the
construction of new water pipes and a school, better streets and
the reorganization of the police, in response to the "increased demands of the new era." The older ones hesitated and warned, fear-
ing higher taxes. Certainly, they admitted, Alamogordo had
grown since "the day of the bomb." It had acquired hundreds of
new residents, but these were not in reality new citizens, merely
the families of soldiers, technicians or building workers with jobs
on the various new reservations such as Holloman Air Force Base
or White Sands. The Defense Department ought to take care of
them, the state provide funds for increased public facilities. "We
didn't ask them to come," ran the argument. "We don't even
make a profit out of them as they buy nearly everything in the PX

military stores." The publicans also complained: "The GI's hardly drink anything here. Saturday nights they go over the border at El Paso into Mexico. There you get cheap whisky, gambling houses and brothels. We can't compete."

Disproportionately deeper are the social effects of the atomic age on the Indian pueblos. "What neither centuries of Christian missionary work nor the efforts of the American administration— first violent, later enlightened—succeeded in doing, technology and the dollar have accomplished in a couple of years," Miss Kuhrtz told me as we accompanied a pregnant woman of the Tesuque pueblos to the Indian hospital at Albuquerque. "The political and religious habits of the race are deeply shaken and will perhaps not outlive the generation at present disappearing."

It started during the Second World War when natives of this part of New Mexico were employed for building work on the atom and rocket installations. They often earned as much at this in one month as they formerly had in a year of farming and cattle raising. Even the women, who worked as servants in the military reservations, now brought more dollars home than they had ever before so much as laid eyes on. At first these sums were paid, according to ancient custom, into the community chest run by the village and the heads of families. But at the end of the war the GI's returned from military service and began to rebel against the old customs. The workmen and household helps in White Sands, Los Alamos or Sandia were soon contributing only a part of their pay envelopes to the pueblo, and even threatened to keep all the money for themselves if the Council of Elders did not "do something" with the dollars paid into the community chest.

Added to this, electric light was installed in various pueblos at the beginning of the atomic age, modern irrigation installations began to replace the old canal systems, agricultural machinery made its appearance. Then came trucks, radios and even telephones, and with each step forward in material adaptation to the American way of life the revision of the old values also advanced. The younger members of the pueblos demanded and received more voice in affairs. Those for whom the concessions of the elders did not suffice broke away altogether from the village union in order to live in the newly founded workers' settlements such as White Rock, quite free from all the old ties and laws. "The new generation no longer believes in the religion of its fathers and ancestors, based on the expectation of rain and the inevitability of destiny," a professor of the University of New Mexico summed it up for me. "It has been won over to the 'money and results' principle of the white world around it." That is the social by-product of the atomic age in New Mexico.

After the long-awaited "clearance" had materialized from somewhere in the bureau beyond, they gave me a soldier as a companion on my visit to the atomic crater. This healthy square-built boy simply could not understand why anyone should expend so much patience on seeing this "bit of nothing in the middle of nothing at all."

After he had led me to the barbed-wire-enclosed rim of the large, astonishingly flat sand plateau which had come into being when the first bomb was released from the thirty-seven-foot-high control tower on zero point of the testing ground, he returned to his seat at the wheel of his jeep and thumbed over the colored pages of his comics.

The crater was covered in many places by a green mineral layer like a sort of scurf, formed in the seething white fire of the explosion. They call this slime-colored lamina "trinitite"—"trinity stone"— after the code word "Trinity" by which the first trial, in 1945, was designated. Splinters of trinitite, sealed in transparent plastic, are secretly sold as souvenirs round about Alamogordo. My armed escort carried one of these tiny symbols of the times with him in his wallet together with the photos of parents, relatives and a variety of girl friends.

If one picks up the trinity stone it crumbles with surprising speed. This has been a help to the desert grasses, mosses, cow parsley and other vegetation which have grown here in the wilderness since time immemorial. In the few years that have passed since the test, plants have been able to break through the glassy green layer of death in a thousand places. In another few years they will fill the entire crater.

"Drop that thing!" the Cerberus called to me. "It's still live." I obediently let drop my radioactive bit of trinitite, threw a last glance at the large ugly scar and turned to go. "Can't think why they don't simply fill the thing up," said the GI. "Such a nuisance." With that we started on our return journey.

MEN AND ROCKETS

Las Cruces, New Mexico

THE White Sands Proving Ground, a strip of land approximately a hundred miles long and thirty-six miles wide, serving for rocket experiments, is a treeless waste as flat as an immense billiard table, its surface, instead of green, being chalk white. Alamogordo and Las Cruces, its two nearest neighbors, are forty minutes' to an hour's drive from the rocket settlement itself, which, since its foundation in 1943, has been growing year by year. Otherwise there is scarcely a habitation to be found in this Godforsaken spot. This is the factor which dictated its choice. For if a rocket were to deviate from its course even for a split second, the deflection or "side step" would, because of the prodigious speeds attained by the latest models, be calculable in dozens of miles.

The shooting ground is enclosed on both sides by high unscaled mountain ranges referred to somewhat disrespectfully by the rocketeers as the "right hedge" and "left hedge." If you consider that the rockets launched from White Sands have reached heights of over 250 miles, the mountains can scarcely claim by this measure to be even hedges; molehills, at best.

The driver who brought me out here to the proving ground from El Paso, the seat of its military administration, was the son of a former stage coach owner. He remembered his father, long ago, at the top of the St. Augustine Pass, pointing to the region of the present shooting ramp. "Down there's where the bandits and cattle thieves used to hide," he told his son. "Over there was the hideout of the toughest of the lot, Billy the Kid."

23

This called to my mind the remark of a scientist whom I had met
not long ago at another rocket experimental station, the Guided
Missile Center of Inyokern on the China Lake. Waving his hand
from the threshold of the laboratory toward the dun-colored waste
around us, he had said, "Our experiments have grown so dangerous
that we've had to withdraw nearly everywhere into regions once
inhabited only by outlaws. Who knows whether we shan't come to
the same sort of end? Captured, lynched, hanged—perhaps society
will want to make us the scapegoats for all this damage, 'in the
name of the law' of righteousness."

In fact, many of the best physicists, chemists, mathematicians,
engineers and technicians are banished today into the most inhos-
pitable sections of America: preferably where, as far as one can
tell, nothing will ever grow, and traces of human existence are at a
minimum. In the wastelands once rejected by covered-wagon
parties in search of new homesteads we now find the modern man
fraternizing with the enemies of life.

The regular inhabitants of White Sands often suffer from a sort of
desert *cafard* and wish themselves back in the good old days of
merely mechanical civilization with its juke boxes, illuminated advertising, gasoline pumps and other similar toys. How colorful, gay
and cosy it seems compared with the world of rockets shooting
into icy spaces. To the uninitiated visitor White Sands presents, not
its monotonous everyday face, but its holiday mien of towering
grandeur. Above the Organ Mountains to the left stream the rays
from a whitish violet crown of light like an overlarge sun. The pillars of rock do, in fact, resemble organ pipes. Sometimes the desert
wind plays upon these gigantic instruments. Then the human beings
creep into their bungalows and huts, while the silvery mountain
lions, small, supple wildcats, descend from their lairs to the arid
mesquite-covered plain. Thunder rumbles more loudly than the
loudest rocket release: the spirit of the nomadic hunter revisits the
testing ground.

But such moods of the weather are extremely rare. At least three
hundred days a year the sky is impeccably blue. Yet this is a blue

with no bloom upon it, with something, instead, of a metallic reflection. As if the large vault had just been delivered from the factory; flawless, reliable and of practically unlimited durability.

Most of the glass roofs of the White Sands workshops have also been painted in some variety of this blue. I found it difficult to accustom myself, out here in the desert, to a genuine little factory town with power stations, water towers, assembly rooms in which there are turning lathes, grinding and welding apparatus, pressing and measuring implements of every description. Though the metal skins, hearts, nerve fibers and brain cells of the large birds that fly up from this nest are produced in other factories and delivered to White Sands, it is here that the separate pieces are assembled, repairs carried out and—according to the nature of the experiment —all sorts of alterations made.

Even a superficial glance at the workshops reveals a different class of workman on the job than is met with in the centers of mass production. The faces of the men at the benches seem more alert and interested than those, for instance, in the large aircraft factory where models are turned out wholesale. The setting up of rockets is still in its early stages; each of the large ones is unique, a particular being with personal characteristics and often unforeseeable humors.

Therefore, each rocket assembled and launched at White Sands receives, in addition to its colorless official number, a personal nickname. It may be christened merely *Number* 25 by the military bureau. The mounters will call it "Slim Lucy" or "One-legged Joe." Animal names find particular favor. In rocketeers' parlance all guided missiles are birds. With a fine disregard for zoological discrepancies, some birds are endowed with names such as "Bumble Bee," "Scotch Terrier" or "Purple Cow." With certain types of small guided missiles the unofficial names have clung. Thus we meet later with an official "Mighty Mouse" or "Holy Moses."

Most of the names devised in the White Sands workshops must be restricted to internal use owing to a bluntness which would cause scandal in general society. The testing grounds and laboratories possess a sort of scatology of their own. There the gigantic instruments for the conquest of space take on the intimate dimensions of the bedroom, and the superhuman meets the all-too-human, at least in its erotic context.

A peculiarity of the language of American rocketeers is its use of technical expressions taken over bodily from the German. Words such as the *Meilerwagen,* a special implement invented during the Second World War in Peenemünde for the transport of V-weapons, or the *Mischgerät,* an important piece of the rocket motor, belong to the language of these workmen just as certain American slang expressions belong to the jazz fans of the entire world. Fashion and gallantry cannot manage without a few crumbs of French, sport without English, the opera without a loan from the Italian. But the technical language of the rocket specialist and future space navigator, born in the chaos of war, is shot through with German.

This small industrial town in the New Mexican desert harbors three fundamentally different professional classes. First the military of the Army Ordnance Corps; these are the virtual masters of White Sands and to them fall all the tasks of organization. Next the engineers, installers and mounters, to whom are assigned the preparation and technical execution of the tests: they are employed by large private firms working on commission for the Army, Navy or Air Force. Each armed service has its own rocket program and proving grounds, but for tests aiming at exceptional heights they share the use of White Sands (much as in small American communities various Protestant sects share the use of one church). And thirdly the scientists.

The most frequent variations occur in this latter group, for whose researches the expensive trial shots into the stratosphere and beyond are carried out. While the soldiers and technicians tend to regard the service in White Sands as a burden and to have little sympathy for "rocket romanticism," the research workers seem only too glad to put up with all the privations and hardships of life in an outpost of civilization.

There is, for example, the biophysicist who entrusts the most varied kinds of passengers to the rockets on their flights: such as fruit flies, bacteria-saturated solutions and occasionally mice or even monkeys. He studies primarily the effect of cosmic rays on the organisms upon which he is experimenting. A colleague of his sends as luggage in the hollow space at the front, which in wartime would be filled with explosives, little bags of cotton wool, corn and grain seedlings. He has already sent more than six hundred varieties of seeds and plants to "the upper stories." Once he mislaid his sample in the moment before the take-off and a special messenger was rushed to a seed store in Las Cruces to obtain a substitute.

A whole series of universities and specialized research institutes make use of the rockets as flying laboratories. They want to explore the temperature, the molecular density, the electrical tension, the light conditions, the average size and frequency of meteor swarms, degrees of moisture in various strata of the atmosphere, alterations in the sun spectrum and a host of other particulars. Every rocket starts on its unpiloted journey packed with pressure gauges, cloud chambers, Geiger counters, spectrographs and other special instruments. Since man himself is unable to go as an observer to regions 50 to 250 or more miles above the earth's surface, whole batteries of artificial eyes, ears and noses, the most sensitive organs of touch and smell, make the journey to heaven in his stead. What they hear, smell, feel, see, is recorded in the course of the journey on sensitized paper, sound strip, films, emulsions and graphic scales, and brought back again to earth.

Looking at the hieroglyphics in which these instruments note down information about their experience, I was struck by the way in which such technically produced sense organs are able to express themselves in their own particular forms of speech and writing. The various long lines which a counting machine writes down for the measurement of cosmic rays or the signs not unlike Arabian scroll lettering with which a highly sensitive pressure gauge tells of its experience in the stratosphere are accurately expressed observations which have to be translated from the language of instruments to that of human beings.

The same minimal oscillation of volts with which the instruments give their information in writing may also be recorded in sounds. The mechanical observers then "tell" in their sung language composed of piping, rumbling, chirping and yowling how high the rocket now is, whether it is following the prescribed course, how strong is the air resistance, and a mass of other details. These pieces of information are best transmitted during flight over so-called "telemeter radio" running to the ground stations where they are recorded on a sound strip. Thus one may obtain complete reports by ear in the electric-pulse language. One like myself, who listens without understanding the meaning of the separate signals, imagines himself to be hearing a piece of modern music.

The music of the spheres is not as sweet and seductive as the Greeks believed, yet it is full of surprising harmonies, strange rhythms and disturbing dissonances. Is this how the angels sing—or how the damned cry?

Anyone driving from Las Cruces on a Wednesday night at about ten or eleven and approaching Alamogordo along Route No. 70 can glimpse on his right, when he reaches the top of the St. Augustine Pass, a vision of the future. If he turns his field glasses onto the brightly illuminated point which, visible at a great distance, rises from the dark plain, he will see a gigantic white cylinder in a tall frame of steel cranes and metal staircases upon which small beings move to and fro. In the glaring light of reflectors they resemble swift lizards creeping back and forth in a kind of overbright moonlight round a heathen totem pole.

That is the rocket being prepared for its launching early tomorrow morning. It frequently takes weeks before the preparations for a single "test shot" can be completed. Every effort to establish a fixed timetable miscarries. Only the weekday for all "test shots" remains the same. This, by arrangement with the local authorities and the neighbors, is always a Thursday. It is most unlikely that a rocket will, as happened in an early experiment, shoot out over one of the two "hedges." But one never can tell, and the few cattle owners in a radius of about fifty miles prefer not to allow their herds into that area on the day of a test. They would rather pocket their compensation and go to El Paso for a day's shopping.

On Wednesday afternoon I had been able to see the shooting

ramp from close by. It is eleven and a half miles away from the
workshops and lodgings: solid, enormous, cement-gray. As strange
and inhuman as a pyramid, as unapproachable and secretive as the
Sphinx. The prow, made of the hardest material, fixed into the
ground, here and there shines like a mirror. These are the spots
which, at the time of previous shots, were transformed by the
immense heat of the rocket's take-off into a sort of braided glass.
At two or three other places, large "peacock's eyes" are shimmering, metallic, iridescent, accidental color mixtures of almost mys-
tic power. They have violet tones in them, otherwise visible only at
the innermost core of a flame, nuances between copper green and
cobalt blue such as emerge in the border zones of fire and solid material. Such spectra are etched into the hard stone ground by the
vaporous mixture of acid fuel gases.

Beneath this starting mat is a rootlike tangle of tubes and wiring
of every description. A square sector of it is lying open. Two uniformed technicians with headphones and a portable X-ray instrument are searching for minute flaws. Other testers are still hanging
high above us with half their bodies inside the rocket. From the loud
speaker directions ring out in the esoteric jargon of the rocketeers:
"Four mega too many. . . . The cheese box stinks. Point seventeen: you need more juice. . . . Hello 'widow walk.' Hello: put
in a different soul. . . ."

The voice comes from Blockhouse 1, a massive windowless
structure full of contact levers and control boards on which red,
green, milk-colored and orange signal lights twinkle on and off,
tension needles dance, white ghosts of light glide over radar screens.
In here, protected by walls forty inches thick against the possibility
of a misdirected start, the contact buttons will tomorrow morning
be connected with the priming. I have only a moment to linger in
this medley of instruments, with its reek of burning, characteristic
of certain kinds of power station. No one looks at the foreign civilian. The eyes of the five or six men at the control dials are entirely
fixed on their task, their lips move very softly as in a prayer which,
conveyed by microphones and loud-speaker to the various platforms of the rocket crane, emerges something like this: "Move the

carbon float once more . . . twelve point three. . . . Okay, you
can cut out the eyes now. . . . Station five: your gremlins are
back again. . . ."

Thus I make my first acquaintance with the gremlins. These, it
is explained, are the goblins of the technical era. They are the spirits
who out of sheer mischief bring about short circuits, bore holes in
gasoline tanks, cause explosions for the fun of the noise. Whenever
a machine misfires or an apparatus won't function, it is the fault
of the gremlins. They were first noticed by the Royal Air Force during the Second World War; presently the Americans claimed
gremlins of their own, and after the newspapers had begun reporting
on the malicious little sprites, they were soon detected in the motor
of every car, in every power station, in every factory. They hover
like will-o'-the-wisps over faulty high-tension wires, scream in
brakes that are applied too late and roar with scornful laughter in
bursting oil tanks. They are the demons in the thick forest of oil
towers, silvery refineries and bare telegraph poles. Swift as electrons,
smaller than the mesons at the core of the atom, they are to be
found wherever the boss of the works rears his mechanical, imitation nature.

Such a gremlin seems now to have played a joke with one of the
thousand minute brain cells of the gigantic bird who is to fly tomorrow morning. For weeks the trial has been in preparation, nearly a
thousand persons have been working to bring it to completion. Now,
within a few hours of the start, it rests with one man to say whether
the test may take place. Only if he succeeds with the delicate operation in Room 17 of the electrical laboratory will Irene—so the
missile has been christened after a popular-song hit—be able to
start.

"We're waiting," says the voice from the other side of the intercom system which extends into every workroom.

"Don't rush me," answers the man in Number 17 into the talking
box fixed above his work table.

Irritably he switches off and bends again over the tiny thing he is holding in a pair of tweezers. He is no longer young and his hands tremble. But there is no one who can replace him, none who can find his way so swiftly and surely about the Lilliputian world of miniature controls as he. He is now trying vainly with a second tweezer to get something scarcely visible to the naked eye on to the coil the size of a pin's head in his left hand, and there to thread it.

"I hate it when people don't let me work in peace," he says and nervously drops both his hands. "It simply won't go."

The workroom is bathed in the artificial sunshine of daylight lamps. No tiny mote dances here, there is not the slightest breath of air, no smoke, no noise. Numerous magnetic slits attract any particle in the air, a thousand infinitesimal holes in the apple-green washed walls suck up every sound. Foam rubber, cork, insulation strips of felt and plastic entirely seal off the room from the outer world: ideal working conditions, almost complete elimination of every sort of disturbance.

The heavy breathing of the man at the table is becoming more even. He is trying his luck again; he passes his hand across the faded skin of his forehead, sighs, picks up both tweezers, then puts them down and looks helplessly, almost imploringly, at the three visitors who have been watching him.

We think we understand, and begin to leave on tiptoe. But he detains us. No, we are welcome to stay. It wasn't the strangers in his workroom that were making him nervous, only the strain and the responsibility. As if to relax his thoughts he allows us, one by one, to look through the curious magnifying glass which he wears on a conspicuous clamp astride his nose. Seen through this lens the two ends of the tweezers on the electric assembly table seem like massive blacksmith's tongs. Between the jaws of the right-hand tweezer lies a thin wire which is to be attached to a coil. Even in this considerable enlargement the wire seems no thicker than a human hair.

If, however, one holds a real hair under the lens it seems as thick as a straw—far too thick for the Lilliputian world of rocket brain centers. For here there are induction coils the size of the head of a needle, which nevertheless can carry dozens of wire reels, there are radio valves as small as peas, transformers no longer than half a cigarette, and a whole ten-valve series that takes up no more space than a matchbox.

"Subminiaturization" is the name given by the specialists to this development caused by the need of guided missiles for ever-smaller current conductors and transformers. Only because more and more and ever finer electronic nerves and cells can be fitted into the scanty space available inside the rocket is it possible to control the projectile with increasing accuracy and make it yield more detailed reports.

The artificial organs of thought, sense and speech have undoubtedly enhanced the "intelligence" of the guided missiles, but also their dependence on their human masters. The more receptive and sensitive they become, the more they implicate their controllers. The earlier V-2 projectiles had still the freedom to deviate from one of the prescribed curves. A more advanced American model, even if it rises hundreds of miles, is dependent on radio signal links and two-way messages exchanged between its mechanisms and those on the earth. And even after its crash, a sound strip may be telling what the rocket experienced and perceived during its brief rise and subsequent fall to death.

Again there is complete silence in the overbright laboratory. The master of the Lilliputian world is holding his breath. Both his hands seem to have petrified. Only one of the two pincers is moving, almost imperceptibly. Suddenly tweezers, fingers, hands again begin to shake furiously. Two greatly magnified pupils look at us through his cyclopean eye and he swears, "That bastard."

But his laugh proclaims that this time he has managed to outwit the tremor. He snaps the intercom on and reports: "Okay. It's yours." His forehead is beaded with sweat.

"Attention. . . . It is now x minus 360 minutes," announces the loud-speaker. One o'clock in the morning and no one in White Sands has gone to sleep. In the canteen, coffee will be served throughout the night and the juke box will play all its repertoire of fifty before daybreak. The observers who are to watch the flight of Irene from the mountains, where the higher observation posts are located, pick up their rations. Soon we hear the buzz of the jeeps in which they are driving through the dark to the beginning of the mountain path. Searchlights stir up the prairie dogs. But the coyotes refuse to be put out; as on every other night, they bay at the moon, the desert, the loneliness and the distant stars. X moment is still six hours away.

"Attention: x *minus* 180 *minutes.*" Dawn is breaking. In a sky like a sheet of blank gray paper the balloons of the aerological unit appear like blots of ink. They are to provide last-minute data concerning air currents and the development of the weather.

"Attention: x *minus* 150 *minutes.*" A dark red tanker truck has arrived at the foot of the shooting ramp. It is known in White Sands as "the whisky pump" because it contains nearly a hundred per cent pure alcohol.

"Attention: x *minus* 125 *minutes.*" Behind the organ pipes of the Organ Mountains the sky is brightening. The forward tanks of the rocket are being filled with alcohol. On the various platforms of the crane about thirty people are still at work. In particular the three-cornered antenna of the telemeter-sender and the carburetor controls of the propulsion fluid are being examined. The loudspeaker apparatus with its thirty or forty connections is also undergoing a routine check-up. The announcer begins with the customary recitation of the key words of the wireless alphabet: "Able . . . Baker . . ." He finds this too boring and bursts instead into a yodel no doubt picked up during his service abroad.

"*X minus* 105 *minutes.*" Figures in transparent milky-blue coats busy themselves about the rocket. Over their faces they wear a sort of plastic veil. Their hands, in which they are carrying pipe lines leading from large steel bottles covered in whitish mist, are encased in long black rubber gloves. A fire engine has also driven up. A "researcher" from an Ohio university, who is sitting next to me, begins to take hope. He has given the rocket a spectrometer to carry along, which he hopes will analyze the sun's rays for him from the highest point of its ascent. Three times the young investigator has been disappointed. Once the start was postponed, another time his instrument had to be unloaded at the last minute to lighten the rocket's ballast, and the third time the spectrometer's trigger device failed. "When the fire department turns up," said this expert, "it means the shooting's really on."

"*X minus* 70 *minutes.*" The rocket has "tanked" 10,800 pounds of liquid oxygen ("lox" the rocketeers call it, for short and in a double sense, "lox" being the name of the smoked salmon offered by New York's delicatessen stores). But the masked men of the propulsion crew are not yet ready. Now they are pumping sodium permanganate, nitric acid and hydrogen peroxide ("the stuff ladies bleach their hair with," comments my knowledgeable neighbor) into the gigantic missile. As the chemicals are dangerous to manipulate ("a handful of sawdust in the high percentage hydrogen peroxide, and bang . . . there'd be a first-class explosion"), all visitors must evacuate Region A, the immediate vicinity of the rocket. We are conveyed in jeeps to one of the many tracking stations which will follow Irene's flight by means of telescopes, cameras and radar apparatus.

"*X minus* 50 *minutes.*" The morning sun has now reached the white rocket, slender and elegant rather than massive in form. We look through field glasses at the high platforms rolling away. For about two minutes the missile stands perpendicular, quite alone against the blue sky. Then we see that a guide line still connects it with a mobile electric power pump. Now a couple of thin folding ladders are being cranked up for possible final intervention. These are the "German ladders," an inheritance from the weapon-experiment station at Peenemünde. The masked crew has also drawn back. The conductors of the experiment seem to have retired behind the gray walls of the blockhouse. The loud-speakers announce "Clear Zone B."

"*X minus* 45 *minutes.*" Measures are being taken to close off Route Number 70. The short stretch which cuts through the proving ground is cleared by the military police. On either side of it, near Las Cruces and on the outskirts of Alamogordo, tourists with field glasses have taken up positions. Two full sight-seeing cars have arrived from El Paso. Strangers used to be allowed to visit the little rocket museum in White Sands and see films of the early test. But since the security regulations have been tightened, the museum with its exhibits (chiefly metal entrails of old V-2's) is also "restricted."

"*X minus* 30 *minutes.*" Mechanics are again working on the rocket. They bring explosive charges which will go off shortly before the falling rocket touches ground. It will then break up into three fragments. This will lessen the impact.

"*X minus* 30 *minutes.*" Again? Did we hear wrong? We were at this point ten minutes ago. The Ohio researcher's face falls. He knows what that means: postponement of the start. "If we're out of luck it'll be '*x* minus 60 minutes' next time," he prophesies, "and back at a snail's pace to '*x* minus 360,' till they finally announce 'No start.' And the whole thing will be put off until next Thursday at the earliest."

The tension has relaxed. The announcer gives incomprehensible technical information. Other voices break in. Somewhere something is not in order.

"*X minus* 15 *minutes,*" announces the monotonous voice from the loud-speaker. The error must have been corrected. The telemeter man at our observation post nods to us: all in order. A smoke wreath is rising over the blockhouse. The observer planes from near-by Contrin Airfield rumble high above us. They are reconnoitering in case man or beast should have strayed into the shooting ground.

"*X minus* 5 *minutes.*" The waiting begins to be unendurable. Hundreds of human eyes, photographic plates, electronic implements, highly sensitive lenses look down from the gigantic amphitheater upon the mute heroine ready for the sacrifice in an arena ringed round with shimmering reddish mountains.

"*X minus* 4 *minutes.*" The receiving implements at our station are humming. They are ready. They are in communication with the sending implements in the sharp nose of the rocket.

"*X minus* 3 *minutes.*" The "umbilical cord" between the missile and the filling apparatus is broken, the small ring holder on the underside of the head falls away.

"*X minus* 2 *minutes.*" A loud siren signal. A cluster of red stars

—the absolutely final warning—is fired over the shooting stand.

"X minus 60 seconds." At all observation posts final preparations. The sun is now directly above the desert and the mountains. All color is blotted from the landscape. It seems pale, as though bled dry. The rocket is quite still in the sharp light, while the loudspeaker begins to recite the seconds:

"Minus 50."

"Minus 40."

"Minus 30."

"Minus 20."

"Minus 10."

"Five,

"Three,

"Two, and . . .

"FIRE!"

But the rocket is still in the same place. Will she refuse to rise? She trembles. She cries out in an uncanny, thrilling tone which comes to us from miles away. Yes . . . a quivering purple flame flashes out of her. She is standing above her pedestal on a twenty-yard long tail of fire. She is no larger than an airplane—a pebble—a speck of dust. She has vanished in the blue of heaven.

With the men of White Sands, however, Irene still keeps contact. They listen to her radio signals, follow her course into ever higher regions. She has long ago passed through the zone of icy cold and is flying at a tearing speed through rising temperatures toward the sun. She meets the gray of heaven's shallows: electrical discharges beat against her hull, meteor particles threaten to collide with her, the blue of heaven has dyed itself into the black of night, the atmosphere has grown so thin that it will no longer grip her delicate tail fins.

The university man from Ohio is holding a map of the sky in front of him, on which the great blue canopy is divided into layers and regions: "Layer D . . . , Layer F . . . , Layer F, 1. . . ." He shows with pencil dots where the rocket may reach its highest point: 110 miles, perhaps even 130 if it attains the present record for its class. A second small rocket of the "WAC Corporal" type which rode on the back of a large missile and was then fired off from a great altitude pushed on to twice that height, on toward the boundaries of space.

The telemeter man beside us reports: "Don't hear anything; it's stopped."

His neighbor of the echo apparatus: "Already on the way back. . . ."

"Then she reached eighty miles at most. . . ." someone surmises.

The man from Ohio is quite crushed. "Only eighty?" he asks. "Really? That won't tell us anything new. We already have spectral measurements up to a hundred miles."

From a distance a hollow sound reaches us. This must be the descending rocket. The jeeps of the Recovery Division, who secure the ruins of a rocket with its valuable cargo of instruments, are already under way.

The loud-speaker has found its voice again and is giving directions to which nobody pays much attention. What went wrong, everyone is wondering? Why did Irene crash after eighty miles? A short circuit? I think of the Cyclops with the trembling hands. Can it be the fault of that infinitesimal piece he was repairing? Did a gremlin ride along into the sky?

Through the telescope we see people running toward the empty shooting ramp. One doesn't hear them at this distance, one only sees them moving: a school of fish stirred up at the bottom of the ocean of air.

My neighbor hangs his head. "Well," he finally says, "try, try again. Someday it's got to succeed."

NO TIME FOR EMOTIONS

Omaha, Nebraska

OMAHA, NEBRASKA, is a city of two hundred thousand or so inhabitants. But in New York, in Chicago or Los Angeles they speak of it as though it were a typical small provincial town somewhere in the backwoods. It is, in fact, a long time since there were any woods in or near Omaha. It lies at the center of the fertile flat Middle Western farm land. A casual collection of asphalt streets and urban houses —even a few skyscrapers among them—grows with a rather comic incongruity out of the endless green and yellow of the fields. For there must be some place where the cattle can be sold and slaughtered, the harvest insured and bargained for, where trains, on their long journeys from East to West and from the Pacific to the Atlantic, may refill with coal and water and change their engines. Thus Omaha arose, grew and prospered, a city everybody needs and no one values.

Still more unnatural is the effect in these rural surroundings of the collection of flat modern buildings on the outskirts of the town. They are out of keeping with the cozy red barns, the lazy arms of the windmills and the plump silos. Like sheets of ice which do not melt even on the hottest days of July, a few landing strips lie in the midst of the shining grainfields. The Latin motto of this settlement may be read on a coat of arms directly beside the entrance. It says, "MORS AB ALTO"—"Death from above."

Offutt Field is the name of this bit of the *newest world* in fertile Nebraska. A military airfield, like dozens of other American air bases built since 1941, it was named after a pilot who crashed to his death. It is an airfield, however, of quite exceptional significance, possibly the most fateful in the U.S.A. For in these brand-new though unpretentious office buildings, leaning against some disused cavalry barracks, are to be found the headquarters of Strategic Air Command, to which, in case of war, the direction of all overseas bomber action is entrusted. Here, in the heart of rural America, is the central point of a system of strong points spread over five continents. And each of these distant strong points may be reached by air almost as quickly as the transcontinental express train, which stops at Omaha, takes to reach either coast of America.

One's impression on entering the pleasantly air-conditioned offices of Offutt Field is far from being either oppressive or pregnant with history. American military installations seldom produce the gloomy and sinister effect of European barracks. Even here, where the general in command is notorious for his severe discipline, the atmosphere suggests a country club.

The officer of the day is on the telephone to Seattle, and the matter in hand seems to be not the transportation of bombs but the arrangements for the week end. "Of course we'll bring along fishing tackle," the man in khaki is saying enthusiastically. "And you over there see to the movie camera. Color film. . . . Yes, absolutely . . . and another thing: the general doesn't drink Scotch. He's a one hundred per cent bourbon man. Okeydoke. *Hasta mañana.*"

Through the open door to the office a broad-shouldered, rather burly officer has entered. He looks neither right nor left, neither at the lanky redheaded adjutant who has followed him with a handful of papers to be signed, nor at the pretty blonde secretary who would like to attract his notice, and certainly not at the foreign civilian who is waiting before a map of the world. This is drawn in a new and unusual manner. Here are the United States, not, as usual, on the western side of the map, but plumb in the middle, and round about it toward the edges of the map, the other continents meekly group themselves. Almost exactly in the middle of the United States is a black dot, under which the words *Offutt Field* (*Omaha*) are to be read. And in the middle of Offutt Field, at the center of all continents, oceans and islands, stands this thick-set chunk of a man who does not even remove the cigar from his mouth as he announces, "Nothing doing with Seattle, Kalberer. Call it off. I must take a run to Washington, they're cooking up something against us again in the Senate Committee." That, of course, was the general. Everyone here is afraid of him but praises his results. What a damned good slave driver, they say. How he got the SAC into shape. How he won't stand for any breach of discipline. How well informed he is on every detail from Alaska to Arabia, from Morocco to Okinawa. "He prefers," they say, "to be informed of the state of his world-wide command in brief and precise figures: 6 per cent more costs in the 15th Air Force, 18 per cent less flight performance in the 6th Air Force, 8 per cent replacement of material necessary per month, only 0.4 per cent casualties in men and machines during the past year."

"His calculations are utterly divorced from feeling. When he ordered the Flying Fortress pilots, who attacked Japan under his command in the Second World War, to fly closer to their targets, the average casualties for each raid rose by a hundred per cent. But the arithmetical problem came out right," Press Adjutant Kalberer, His Master's Voice, explained to me: "If, in the course of one attack, a third of our bombers were lost, but at the same time the number of direct hits was doubled, it was cheaper than two weeks with one-fifth losses in each."

The big four-to-ten-engine bombers under the command of the general are not stationed at Offutt Field itself. Here only those machines land in which he embarks on his flights of inspection round the world. "I know sixty countries," the boss tells his admirers in moments of relaxation. Most of the countries he knows only from the air or from brief landings at one of the air bases. These strong points resemble each other much as one chess board resembles the next: the same runs, the same hangars, the same food in the canteens, the same military faces which greet the visiting chief with the same standard words, whether it happens to be North Africa, North Bavaria or North Japan. "No superfluous words, please, the general doesn't like excuses and complaints." A favorite saying of his is, "Results are what count. It's all one to me whether a mission goes phut out of hard luck or out of inefficiency!"

But the general gets the best survey of his "magnesium monsters," as he calls his bombers, with rough tenderness, when he is at home, that is at Offutt Field. Every flight strong point in and out of the U.S. is permanently connected with the Electronics Section near Omaha, a windowless building heavily guarded by soldiers ready to shoot, and illuminated day and night by the whitish violet of fluorescent tubes. Here the teleprinters tick running reports on the seventeen large SAC bases in North America, and radiograms and long-distance calls from dozens of foreign flights are received in a room protected by armored doors. Greenland calls, Japan reports, Alaska sends in a weather bulletin. It is three o'clock in the afternoon in Omaha but already ten at night at the English base in East Anglia, three in the morning in Bahrein, five at Port Darwin. It is raining in Siam and Brazil, a sandstorm rages over Libya, on the Aleutians there has been a light snowfall.

Offutt Field keeps records everywhere and orders each bomber's route accordingly. It is proud of its "instant readiness to strike." There is no one in the entire Command, with its thousands of pilots, mechanics, wireless operators, ground staff, whose exact whereabouts on the globe at this precise minute would be unknown. Even a man off duty must report at regular intervals at an appointed place; under no circumstances may he go more than two hours' driving distance from the headquarters of his unit.

Often the long-range bombers of SAC make nonstop training flights of thirty, forty, fifty hours, at an average speed of three hundred to six hundred and seventy-five miles an hour. None of the crew of fourteen (three of whom are pilots) may go to sleep for more than two or three hours. When the machine is cruising at heights of six to ten miles, the use of any of the six sleeping bunks is forbidden, for in case of the pressure cabin's springing a leak, a possibility never altogether to be excluded, the provision of oxygen stored in the body will last only thirteen seconds before unconsciousness sets in. That is too short a time for a person shocked out of slumber to put on and fasten his oxygen mask and get it working.

In these training flights the bombers fly high above the clouds over oceans which they never see, visit strange lands and continents whose contours they perceive at best as fleeting shadows on the radar screen. Without alighting they draw "slipknots" round the diminished globe. They rise, for instance, in a small garrison town in Florida, fly nonstop by way of the North Pole, Latin America or even Arabia back to the U.S.A. and land only a few hundred miles from their starting point, on a military airfield in Texas.

Thus the dizzy speed and sure conquest of distance, the once highly prized mastery of the air, has lost its real meaning: the heavens have become a vast parade ground on which a general gives his orders with the bark of a sergeant major.

Muroc, California

About a hundred miles to the northeast of Los Angeles in the Mojave Desert there exists a series of dried-out lakes so barren, so desolate, so unbearable that not even the desert rats or the coyotes would live in them. For a time during prohibition, whisky was distilled there and brought to the cities. This could be done quite openly because the moonshiners knew that the heat-shy police would leave them undisturbed. But although the profits from the business were considerable, the illegal whisky barons soon took flight. Even a thousand per cent profit did not look tempting if they had to burn in hell during their lifetime.

Then the "hot rodders" discovered the territory. These were young lads with an enthusiasm for automobiles, and a knack for rebuilding old ones into racing cars. With these "hot rods" they began to try for speed records on the hard arid sand of Muroc Lake. The motor fans had, like the whisky distillers, fled the strictures of the law. In the crowded streets and "highways" of Los Angeles they had not been able to quench their thirst for speed without coming into conflict with the police. But out here it was no man's land, belonging only to the prickly cactus and the little dust devils.

When the "hot rodders" invited an air force major by the name of Hap Arnold to one of their races, they made an unforgivable error. For later, when this same officer, in a post of responsibility, was directing the construction and completion of the American Air Arm, he remembered the terrain on the dry lake at Muroc. It appeared to him an ideal natural landing place for aircraft and, moreover, adapted by its remoteness to the testing of new secret types. Quietly, during the Second World War, the state appropriated the tract of land. The "hot rodders" had to look for another dry lake for their races, found Harper's Dry Lake, were soon expelled from there by the Military, and ended with a third salt lake, which they have named "El Mirage" because they do not know whether the new motor paradise may not also prove to be a mirage in an era of hard military realities.

Several "hot rodders" tried later, when they were a little older, to return to their beloved Muroc Lake by volunteering for the U.S. Air Force, especially since the air base established there was used, after the Second World War, for trials of only the fastest flying models. One might have assumed that these boys, with the love of speed in their blood, would have been the stuff of which pilots are made. That is what they thought themselves. But not one of them survived the stiff psychological tests imposed upon candidates for the post of test pilot at Muroc.

For the ideal pilot sought by the American Air Force must not be a speed maniac. One who gets intoxicated with sheer speed will be rejected just as surely as one who gets drunk on a bottle of whisky. The hot rodders are machine romantics, raised by velocity to a state of ecstasy. But a supersonic pilot must be self-controlled, precise and cool—a machine rationalist. One forms an erroneous picture of the jet pilots as foolhardy daredevils, whippets of the ether. Instead one finds heavy, stolid, almost dull types with much more of the pedant than the adventurer about them. Neither do the jet pilots fit the role of Don Juans, which the popular magazine and screen writers would cast them for.

I spoke with the wife of such an ace, who had just returned from the theater of war crowned with fresh laurels. "A jet pilot needs a quiet wife who considers his nerves. He has no time for emotions," she said. "Passionate romances, moods, worries about love, are

things he cannot permit himself. They'd be a mortal danger to him."
She had become acquainted with her husband when he was in a
military hospital. "Russ was looking for a girl that wouldn't excite
him, see?" she said naïvely. "It seems I filled the bill. And then
naturally he wanted a wife who wouldn't be fidgeting about him
when he was on a job. A pal of Russ's had to drop out of the squadron because his wife ruined him for flying. Every evening when he
came home safe she flung her arms round his neck and cried with
joy. So he grew accident-conscious, expected one on every dangerous job, and twice jumped out too soon instead of saving his
machine. That got a bit too expensive for the Air Force."

The typical test pilot living in Edwards Air Force Base on Muroc
Lake is a man at least thirty years of age, if possible even older. A
father of a family with a few gray hairs and possibly even a touch of
corpulence, like Chuck Yeager for instance, who was the first,
on February 12, 1947, to fly over Muroc Dry Lake faster than
sound. Since then dozens of other pilots have been able to break
through the once-dreaded sound barrier, brave the shock waves
making a dam high above them at this speed, and in the scarcely explored zone beyond the sound barrier, resist the insidious dizziness
which was trying to tear from them the control of their machines.

The greatest problem is now the intense heat produced by friction at these speeds. Only with the help of special cooling devices
are the metal wings of the modern Icarus prevented from melting
like wax, and Icarus himself from being incinerated.

Admission to Edwards A.F.B. is naturally conceded to few outsiders. For mine I am indebted to a chance. At a certain time residents of the San Fernando Valley near Los Angeles were awakened
late at night by loud detonations which sounded like the result of
explosions. When these phenomena were repeated in broad daylight
and with increasing force, the inhabitants grew uneasy. A rumor
began to circulate that a new weapon-testing station had been installed in the neighborhood, and protests were raised. Inquiries on
the part of the press were passed over in silence by the competent
military authorities. The result was an increase in the rumors, which
now found nearly universal credence. Finally the local representa-

tives of the armed forces consented to issue an explanation. It was a matter, they said, of a perfectly harmless acoustical phenomenon which occurs when very fast aircraft racing earthward from a great height are suddenly pulled up again to horizontal flight. Into the vacuum created by the jet plane the air tends to rush with a hollow noise.

Well—nobody believed them. People had acquired the habit, since the last war, of listening with skepticism to explanations. Too often ostensibly harmless experiments turned out to be undertakings of equal potential danger to the direct participants and the uninvolved neighbors. Thus, the first atomic explosion in Alamogordo was represented to the chance observers in the near vicinity as "a routine munitions test." In order to prove that in this case there had been no misrepresentation, the military spokesman invited several guests to a demonstration of the phenomenon at Edwards A.F.B. For the first time after a two-year embargo the experimental ground at Muroc Lake, otherwise closed to all press inspection, became accessible for a short time to carefully screened visitors.

As we drove through the Mojave Desert at about five in the morning coming from Los Angeles, we seemed to be in some country of the moon. Now and then between fragments of rock and alkaline sand heaps emerged the silhouette of a Joshua tree, in wild convulsions, stretching its thorny boughs to heaven as if crying for help. Dawn was still breaking when flaming comets' tails suddenly appeared, on the horizon. Over at the base, explained one of our company, the aviation editor of the Los Angeles *Times,* a Lockheed F945, equipped with rockets and additional boosters, had gone up. There, early hours of the morning are particularly favorable for speed trials because the cool air is not so dense and forms less compact shock waves.

The air base itself is disappointing at first glance. Most of the buildings are wooden barracks hurriedly thrown together in wartime, similar, thought a colleague, to hastily erected mining camps of the gold-rush era. To me this military outpost, with its barbedwire fencing and the GI demanding our credentials to the music of his small radio, seemed more like the roughly carpentered entrance to a Displaced Persons' camp, such as I had seen in Europe. The atmosphere in the mess fortified this impression. In long rows the ground staff and mechanics stood half asleep and sullen while their coffee was poured, or waited, with a metal tray, for their rations. They can heat their primitive quarters, as I learned later, only with little oil stoves. But this, in the cold desert nights, is insufficient. Here as in so many other places where America is building up and testing her astonishing technical power potential, the least is done for personal comfort because money for such "inessentials" is granted last, if at all. For the machines, which cost millions of dollars, nothing is too good. But the industrious uniformed worker bees, who serve these exigent metal drones, must often be satisfied with little.

The big runway, by whose sides the gigantic hangars lie, is naturally in faultless order. Smooth, without imperfections, an immense parquet which must daily be rewaxed, because exhaust gases, hot flames, burning paraffin and smoking oil burn holes and other unevennesses in the hard cement.

It was nearly eight in the morning when we were presented at the edge of the starting runway to the test pilots, Major Frank Edwards and Major Askani, both among the first five who ventured after Yeager behind the supersonic wall. A whole battery of oscillographs, microphones and pressure gauges was set up on long tables beside the field, to record the phenomenon of jet detonation while the two flyers let themselves be built into their machines. When I speak of "building in" I mean it literally. The modern supersonic pilot is installed in the machine he is going to fly like an unfortunately still irreplaceable component of its mechanism. From his working uniform connecting lines are carried to the oxygen supply, to the radio equipment, to the radar, to the thermostat controls. In the region of the stomach and in the calf of the leg of his special suit there are small pressure chambers. These are intended to counteract the strongly felt increase in the force of gravity, particularly in sharp swift curves which are measured in "g" units (equal to normal gravity). As soon as too many "g's" drive the blood into the extremities the rubber bubbles of the "g-suit" press it back again.

In the crash helmet clapped on the pilot's head are to be found not only microphones and headphones but also the Plexiglass visor electrically heated against sudden glaciation, an oxygen outfit and a "brain-wave writer" which gives warning, by a little red lamp, of an imminent oxygen shortage before the senses have become conscious of danger.

This entire system of "umbilical cords" is attached to the electric circuit of the machine. Screwed many times over into the organism of his aircraft, constantly guided from the ground by radio, the pilot starts his plane. Charlie Chaplin at a conveyer belt, grumbling against the machine and at the same time plunging the whole law-dictated organization of work into confusion, seems, by comparison with the supersonic pilots, the symbol of a revolt which today would mean certain suicide.

For this new supersonic man is no longer only the machine's opposite number, with a certain measure of freedom and possibility of protest—he has been absorbed by his machine and become a part of it.

It seems as if the machine were evolving toward man. The more highly it is bred the more human attributes does it develop. It reveals unforeseeable sensibilities and moods. As one listens to the starting noise of a jet motor, that almost animal scream, compared with which the stuttering and backfiring of the ordinary combustion motor sounds almost cozy, one cannot get rid of the impression that a living being is trying, through an inarticulate howl, to express itself.

Is it anger? Is it pain? The jet mechanics, generally a trifle deaf in the first place, and subject to a series of peculiar bodily disturbances ascribed by Air Force doctors to the imperceptible overtones of the new machines, are persuaded that they can read something into these sounds. A belief is held by the flyers that the mechanics can nearly always predict ill luck by the starting sound of the machine. It happens not infrequently that a pilot at Edwards A.F.B. asks his chief mechanic, standing beside him during the customary final examination of the machine, "Is she laughing or crying today?"

"She's rocking with laughter," asserts the mechanic.

"Good," says the pilot, "then let's go."

The transparent Plexiglass roof is pushed over his seat, all jump aside in order not to be sucked into the machine by the uncannily strong inhalation of the round air intakes. Without gliding slowly over the runway strip in the manner of older planes, the F86D has risen into the air with lightning speed and is climbing nearly vertically till it has grown as thin as a silver pencil and is making delicate tracery on the clean blue morning sky.

But the pilot's voice is still very near us. As an act of hospitality to the visitors, General Boyd, the commander of the air base, has had the wireless connection with the aircraft pass through a large loud-speaker standing beside the runway. He himself takes over the role of "copilot" at the ground station. And so we all hear Major Askani announcing "Roger, Roger. . . . This is 578. I'm making controls on 33."

So she is now 33,000 feet high. The commander gives routine orders in a quiet voice. Even the most experienced pilot is always given instructions from below so that, taken up as he is with the control of his dozens of instruments, he will be sure to forget nothing in the course of his swift flight.

"Where's Frank?" asks Boyd. "Come in, Frank."

For the second machine, with Frank Everest, has started, too, from another runway.

Everest answers at once: "628 calling. I'm on 42. Slightly northeast of the field, trouble with ice formation."

Boyd: "Full on. We're waiting."

Everest: "628 . . . read . . . going into a dive. . . ."

We hear the breathing of the pilot who is maneuvering somewhere up there in the heavens. He sniffles a bit. Then suddenly he mutters, "Go!"

When he comes out of the dive into the level, we ought to hear the promised thunderclaps. And in fact there they are:

Boom . . . and again: Boom. . . .

The whole battery of instruments shakes, the needles dance wildly. The demonstration has been successful.

"Okay, Frank," Boyd jokes roughly into the microphone. "Now that you've relieved yourself you can come down."

The performance is repeated when Askani, too, carries out his maneuver. This time we not only hear the remarkable explosion but also see the machine, faster than a projectile as it skims the length of the great Dry Lake and swiftly disappears.

Later on, in the conference hall, we again see the two pilots who participated in the test. Tired, pale, and seeming the older for their effort, they are replying to questions. A young specialist in aerodynamics stands at a blackboard illustrating the phenomenon of detonation when General Boyd in the middle of the conference is handed an envelope by a messenger. He opens it and his face takes on an expression of such intensity that nearly everybody is impelled to turn away from the blackboard in his direction.

He looks at us, motions with his hand for silence, and begins to speak:

"I have a piece of bad news to report to you. A jet bomber that went up from our base last night on a practice flight has been found wrecked a few miles from here on Air Base territory. We had lost all wireless connection with it hours ago. A search party has found the fragments of the machine. All eight occupants are dead."

At once the whole scientific demonstration of the morning is forgotten. The reporters smell out a much bigger story. The general is besieged with questions. May one visit the scene of the disaster? What type of model was being tried out? Are the pilots well known? For how many hours has the plane been missing? To each question the same answer is given: "No comment." All have risen from their seats and press round the general and the two pilots who are even whiter than before. No one is looking at the man at the blackboard, who has resignedly laid down his chalk.

POOR LITTLE SUPERMAN

San Antonio, Texas

WHEN I think of contemporary America striving for mastery over nature, the first picture that comes to my mind is of a young man whom I recently met in an aviation medicine laboratory at a California university. No, he was not the freckle-faced, lighthearted college boy whom we have all seen on posters and photographs and on the films. Gladly would I let such a laughing rosy boy, joyous and carefree, march at the head of a parade of memories. But another, whose name I do not even know, thrusts forward instead, and will not be denied; he keeps looking at me out of his cavernous eyes with a vague, nearly distracted gaze. And I must return his glance, see again the compressed lips from which the teeth stand out as in a caricature. How the skull structure has pushed forward against the flesh of the cheeks which are flattened by a tremendous pressure, the skin of the forehead pulled back, the flesh of the chin sagging . . . poor little superman.

He is nearly naked, this boy. Apart from bathing trunks he is wearing nothing but two nylon belts, with which he is fastened to an upholstered seat. The seat is in an open gondola at the outer end of a long inclined arm which is moved at first slowly, then with increasing acceleration, round a central axis. A bell rings shrilly. The unusual roundabout begins to turn faster and faster. The small living bundle up there on the seat goes past at a wild and ever wilder speed. In contrast with the distorted features, the voice of the subject comes clearly through a loud-speaker. He is

51

counting into a microphone. "One . . . Two . . . Three . . . Four . . . Five . . . Six . . . Seven . . . Eight . . . Nine . . . Ten . . . One . . . Two . . . Three . . ."

The voice stops. Silence. Only the swish of the centrifuge. Then, skipping two counts, with the greatest effort comes "s . . ss . ix."

At the moment when all questions have been repelled, when it has become plain that no attempt, however skillful, can draw the military out of their necessary professional reserve—in the moment, therefore, when both sides are silent, thinking perhaps for the first time of the dead lying out there unburied in the glaring sun, something almost inconceivable occurs.

An airplane whizzes through the conference hall. It is a small model resembling the ones we saw at this morning's test, a tiny, colored cardboard affair. It reels once or twice across the room, rebounds from the walls, then dives with a playful "zip." All present are completely surprised by the air attack. We ask ourselves who could have staged this gruesome farce. We see a little chap with a flashlight camera snapping the general and the two test pilots as they bend in astonishment over the cardboard model. One of the soldiers drawn up stiffly at the door emerges from his trance and snatches at the intruder, who has meantime clambered nimbly onto a chair and is releasing three, four, five other tiny machines to whir across the room. An accomplice of the little chap, a press man apparently, raises his arms in entreaty and loudly explains what it is all about. No excitement, please, this is an advertisement for a toy jet, in view of the approaching Christmas season. The sentry receives a sign from the general to get rid of the overzealous publicity agent who had been able, through pull, to smuggle himself into the heavily guarded Base. Everyone has a carton pressed into his hand by the brisk little man, containing a folded airplane model. There is a rigging-up of cardboard wings, and elastic motors. The conference room has become a toy testing ground.

The general and the two pilots have taken advantage of the

tumult quietly to disappear. "Poor old General Boyd," resumes
the much-decorated public-relations officer who shepherds the
flock of newspapermen. "The disaster has really hit him hard.
Think of the paper work the poor man has ahead of him. To begin with, all the condolence letters he'll have to write. . . ."

The steel arm whirls at top speed. And the voice stumbles,
stammers in the sounds of a no-longer-comprehensible language:
"Ave . . . Eiiiiiiiiii . . . TTTaaa . . ."

Again the bell. With a sharp jerk, which in its abrupt ugliness
hurts the onlooker's eye, the large merry-go-round comes to a
stop. The body, pressed to its base with gigantic force by centrifugal power, is now thrown forward in the carrier belt like a
loose bundle.

Two uniformed hospital orderlies are waiting. They release the
unconscious man from his harness, lay him with efficient motions
on a raised stretcher and step back to make way for two men in
white coats and a nurse. Blood-pressure gauges are quickly fastened round his upper arm, electrodes attached to his temples
and knuckles, saliva specimens taken from his tongue with little
glass swabs, a rubber indicator clapped over his mouth; mechanical pencils jerk over highly sensitized paper. They say with their
curves, "his heart beats thus, his brain pulsates thus, his nerves
tremble thus."

Now the young man opens his eyes. "Good boy," says the doctor, then professionally to his assistants and the nurse, "Get ready
for the urine test," and to the experiments director: "Next . . ."

Again the sharp tinkling of the bell. The extraordinary merry-
go-round has a new passenger.

This time something white and furry is squatting in the gondola
at the end of the centrifugal arm and utters loud cries as soon as
the speed increases.

"Scottie's in a bad humor today," says the red-faced Public
Relations Officer who had invited me to a view of this apparatus
for the choice of new fliers. "Yesterday he tried a couple of times
to break his neck. Incredible. Seems he really wanted to commit
suicide. He hates the experiments, can't get used to them."

Again the movement of the gyrating metal arm breaks off like a film.

The occupant of the gondola jerks convulsively in all his limbs and emits a strange dismal sound. No man laments like this, nor any beast. The goat Scottie is no longer either one or the other. He is a laboratory being, a statistical entity, and will figure in a communication "concerning the effects of positive acceleration on a series of warm-blooded animals," one of eighty-seven objects of experiment.

Above Scottie's whimpers, the voice of the machine master announces from the motor cabin:

"Those were 28 g."

"Twenty-eight times force of gravity," remarks somebody. "It's a wonder his head didn't come off at the stop."

The hospital orderlies are back at work again. The doctor bending over the late lamented Scottie states quietly: "Internal bleeding, no wonder."

The bell is ringing again.

Shaken, beaten, kneaded, scalded, frozen, suffocated, crushed; this happens daily to dozens of young Americans. In the Santa Susana Mountains of California they let themselves be tied to a small sled and shot vertically into the air by rocket propulsion; in the Mojave Desert they are whirled by a powered sleigh at meteoric speed on a horizontal rail; in Johnsville, Pennsylvania, they are swung back and forth on a large swing until they lose consciousness; in Ann Arbor, Michigan, they are driven by means of special sound-recording instruments into complete confusion of speech and sense; in Princeton, New Jersey, they lose their equilibrium through contact with supersonic waves. They sit in the ovens of Eglin Air Force Base, Florida, or in the ice chambers of Wright-Patterson Field near Dayton, Ohio; leap from heights of forty thousand feet over the Holloman Air Force Base, New Mexico; let themselves be hurled in cages that fall freely through the depths of the neighboring Carlsbad Cavern. In San Antonio, Texas, they are hermetically sealed in pressure chambers and the air gradually exhausted to simulated altitudes of thirty-five, fifty, sixty thousand feet, in which the blood begins to boil and the nitrogen clots on the surface in the form of skin blisters.

Why do they permit themselves to be so tormented? No tyrant has condemned them to it. No regime wishes to extort confessions from them. Nevertheless they submit themselves to trials such as no torturer could surpass in refinement. And they do so of their own free will. For they have been told, "You are our vanguard. You are the pioneers, the patrols on the frontiers of human capacity and endurance. We must recognize these frontiers clearly since we wish to cross them and have already partially crossed them."

Never before has the human species been subjected to such systematic and searching tests as in the laboratories of American aviation medicine. Here weak flesh is valued only as material. It is examined as objectively and pitilessly as a textile fiber, as a metal alloy. They ask: What pressure will the lungs bear? How hard can knocks be for the bone structure to stand them? How quickly does the eye react? When does fear overcome the spiritual and moral resistance? None of these things shall be left to chance. They even measure pain, with the newly introduced unit, "dolor." They set up an equation for death by freezing, stake out the zone between consciousness and unconsciousness with a stop watch. Even the unbearable, the extreme limits of suffering must be mathematically defined.

All this is happening because the race has set out on its longest journey to an unknown destination. The path leads out of the earthly orbit into regions for which man was probably never intended and for which his organism has not been fitted by nature. Here the will power and superhuman energy displayed by seafarers and explorers of earlier generations are insufficient for survival. The unprotected flier even with the strongest resistance will be unconscious in a maximum of thirteen seconds at a height of fifty-five thousand feet. Since airplanes in recent years can operate ever longer, ever faster and in ever higher strata of air, the doctors have been obliged to deal with many new symptoms of weakness: with transitory or chronic complaints, with quite extraordinary accidents and psychic breakdowns, to which the pilots of the most progressive models are exposed.

And all that is only the beginning. Experimental aircraft have already reached heights of sixty-two thousand feet. But beyond them beckon the regions already reached by unmanned rockets, up to two hundred and fifty miles above the earth. The new branch of space medicine is already concerning itself with the biological and physiological problems of interplanetary traffic. It is trying to ascertain, for example, how the human body will resist the increased gravitational force it will have to bear in the violent speed at which a space ship is fired off. It is studying the effects on the body of the total absence of gravity to be met with outside the orbit of the earth, depriving the "astrogator" of mastery not only over his muscles, but also over his sense of up and down, so that his rise to the unknown stars will seem, through an error of the senses, a fall into bottomless space.

The question being asked throughout these scientific torture chambers is: How can man be fitted to keep pace with his new higher and faster flying machines? Will he remain, as the chief engineer of a large California aircraft firm unflatteringly expressed it to me, "a drag on progress"?

An Air Force instructor whose lectures I attended at the famous academy for flying cadets at Randolph Field formulated this outlook in the following categorical assertion: "Measured by the flying tasks which lie ahead of him, man is a faulty construction."

And eighty cadets noted down the simplification further simplified: "Man . . . a faulty construction."

That man, as he comes forth from the hands of his Maker, should be described as a sort of reject by a specialist in American aviation medicine struck me as a blasphemy. But the thought does not so much as enter the minds of young people being prepared here in San Antonio, by six weeks' courses, for their theoretical examinations as pilots. They have all grown up in the firm conviction that there is nothing—nothing in the world—incapable of progressive betterment by the hand of man: not even man himself.

For the great experience of their lives has been that during the short span of years in which they grew up, more perfect creations were appearing year by year in the machine world around them: automobiles with better motors, television sets with larger screens and clearer pictures, harvesting machines which could imitate hand movements more perfectly. Each year the advertisements for washing machines, razors, lawn mowers, automobile tires and countless other objects have driven home the idea: this year *still* better, *still* more perfect, *still* more complete.

Why, then, should it not be possible also to reconstruct man, to build a "superman model" upon which improvements could be made, if possible, every twelve months as with the make of a car? The faulty construction of the human organism revealed in those painful tests is regarded as an incentive, the tortures endured in laboratory experiments appraised as biological weaknesses which must be overcome.

"Something's simply got to be done to get over these annoying deficiencies," one of the cadets said to me. "They won't stop us."

Behind this determination lies the conviction, confirmed a thousand times over by patent gadgets and machines, "It can be done." For the young American born into the technical world and its annual improvements, this "it can be done" is the fundamental dogma. "No problem is unsolvable," he says. "Nothing is unattainable." These four words "it can be done" are probably more firmly anchored in the soul of the inhabitant of the newest world than the principles of democracy, and more binding than the commands of religion. They are the naïve creed with which he expresses his pretension to universal power.

The School for Aviation and Space Medicine, lodged in a part of the friendly green campus of the air university at Randolph Field near San Antonio, was, until 1939, the only school in the world specializing in aviation medicine. Originally its main work consisted in the choice of suitable military pilots and the instruction of aviation hospital staff. But since technical progress made possible the attainment of new heights and speed, the institute's sphere of activity has been expanded. One of the recently founded departments bears the name of "Human Engineering." But this "art of engineering applied to man" is, in fact, the problem of all sixteen branches of the School for Aviation and Space Medicine.

In more than half a hundred bungalows, laboratories and workshops, over a hundred doctors, biologists, physiologists, neurologists, atomic physicists, supersonic specialists, electron experts, anthropologists and psychologists are trying to evolve a stratospheric man and perhaps even a space man.

Their "methods of production" are in general those employed by industry. They begin by formulating the problem mathematically in figures and algebraic formulas, then proceed to investigate the logical and practical way to its solution. That is the particular task of the biometry department in Randolph Field. Its head, a researcher of under thirty to whom I expressed my amazement, asked: "Why should there not be as close a collaboration between mathematics and medicine as there is between mathematics and engineering? Why should we not represent and logically analyze man the machine in the same impersonal language of symbols as one applies to a flying machine? Much medical progress has been halted on the laborious road of trial and error because of irrelevant scruples. How many millenniums, for example, did it take the cave man to begin protecting himself with fur clothing against the cold, how many more centuries passed before this man exchanged the protection against cold which he carried about with him for a house? In aviation medicine today we are faced with similar problems. An entirely new climate calls for entirely new measures of protection. Biometry can save the investigator from roundabout or wrong paths, can save him many superfluous experiments."

Largely through the intervention of this department a series of efforts at Utopian solutions were hindered from the outset or stopped at an early stage. One of the somewhat theoretical ideas, for example, was by crossbreeding to beget a new race of space-conditioned men. That was immediately excluded probably less because of religious than practical scruples. First, control of heredity in the mass, such as is exercised with increasing sureness upon plants and animals, was not sufficiently advanced. Secondly, these efforts would have required too much time; the production period for breeding this race of pilots would have amounted to at least nine months plus fourteen to eighteen years.

It was slightly less easy to establish the improbability of making pilots "height proof" by injections. It took longer still to convince the heads of the school, reared in the ways of military thought, that their professional skills were inapplicable; results could not be achieved even by the most zealous training of the future stratosphere flier. Certain subjects accustomed themselves gradually to standing in an increased number of "g's," so that they finally learned to endure a tenfold instead of sevenfold increase in the gravitational force. But these increases in performance were far from sufficient. In certain flying maneuvers a much greater load, unbearable even with long training, was required.

So the fact came at last to be recognized that a "stratospheric man" or "space man" could not be reconstructed from the inside out of his own substance, but would have to be acclimatized from without, to the conditions hostile to human life beyond the oxygen frontier and the sound barrier.

The first step was to give the pilot a second pair of "lungs," in the form of oxygen apparatus which in turn themselves developed "illnesses" at very great heights and had to be altered accordingly. Then the pilot was lent a bony structure made of pressure chambers and a new skin in the guise of protective covering. Finally, by built-in electronic implements such as radar, he was provided with organs of sight capable of reacting to approaching objects during supersonic flight far more rapidly than his own sluggish eyes.

The theoretical groundwork for the production of this arsenal of extrahuman prostheses is laid by the studies at Randolph Field and in an increasing number of military testing grounds and laboratories.

On the basis of these experiments there have already been devised, executed and tested, dozens of stratospheric uniforms and space suits, in some cases like the plating of prehistoric saurians, in others like the harness of a medieval knight or a deep-sea diver. Masked, heavily armored, so thickly veiled as to be scarcely able to see, man now soars to the heavens, relying almost entirely on his artificial organs, the electronic guiding instruments. Only thus dare he venture into the newly penetrated, barely conquered regions above his head.

But he is never free of the strong and comprehensible fear that his protective arrangements may fail him. Should his armor be damaged through error or accident, or, as is only too likely with devices evolved primarily for warlike ends, through hostile action, he is handed over practically defenseless to the powers of the empyrean. A single bullet, ripping through the pressure chamber of his aircraft breaks his fragile barrier against a hostile world in which breathing is impossible, where he is as sure of perishing as a fish that has been violently pulled out of its element. It is the age-old fear of the *nothing,* now come true—the *horror vacui* which accompanies him on his newest adventure.

At Randolph Field I saw rescue practice going on. First, the future pilots, crews and nursing sisters charged with unloading the wounded in stratospheric bombers are prepared for the dangers of explosive loss of pressure. They are shut into a long steel tank whose inside may be observed through a bull's-eye and pumped to a simulated height of approximately 33,000 feet.

They were in high spirits, radiant with the joy of life on their "trip to heaven." They laughed and flirted; the experiment was like a parlor game. But then came the moment for which the test had been arranged. The conductor of the experiment bored a hole from the outside through the transparent membrane stretched across the bull's-eye. With a loud bang the air streamed into the pressure chamber. The cabin filled with a milky mist through which one could recognize indistinctly the faces of the inmates. It was their duty in the few seconds of consciousness at their disposal after this event (similar to a fall from the stratosphere) to find, put on and lace their oxygen masks and prepare themselves for the parachute jump.

Seven of the eight participants discharged their task with due precision. But the eighth was apparently so shaken by the simulated explosion as not to find his mask on time. And I had before me once more the distorted face on the merry-go-round. The nursing sisters with their black rubber masks, resembling reptiles more than human beings, bent over the unconscious figure: the new race of stratospheric men exerting itself on behalf of the weak earth man. And on the masks which had now become their faces one could read no pity.

PART THREE

Grasping at the Atom

THE LAST ADVENTURERS

Durango, Colorado

THEY KEEP COMING and coming. Each day new ones arrive. In old automobiles, in buses, by train. Youths and graybeards. Greenhorns and old hands. When the conductor of the Greyhound Bus is admonished by a passenger: "Careful! Please don't throw my luggage about, there are delicate instruments in it," he knows whom he is dealing with. Another uranium hunter. Another chap who thinks he'll dig a million dollars out of the earth in a couple of months.

The delicate object for which the newcomers tremble is the electronic divining rod of our day, a Geiger counter. From the outside it looks not unlike a portable wireless. One hangs it over one's shoulder by a leather strap, plugs in the headphones, takes hold of the rubber-insulated tube and wanders over the landscape. In the headphones there is a continual crackling, knocking and ticking. "That's cosmic radiation," explains the potential uranium king. "Radioactivity. Keeps bombarding us from up there. Day and night. Funny, isn't it?"

The first uranium hunter I met boarded the same bus as I at the Grand Junction railway station. Our common goal was Durango, on the other side of the Rockies at the end of a magnificent mountain road bearing the proud name of "The Million-Dollar Highway." This man had served twelve years in the Navy, then tried for two years, at Sears, Roebuck, the mail-order house, to earn a supplement to the little sum paid him by the State on his retirement.

But it is really too dull handling sewing machines and electric irons in a warehouse when you've been used to working with torpedoes and other explosives. "I read an article on the uranium rush out here in Colorado, and I said to myself right away, 'That's the thing for you, Joe.' D'you know, my grandfather went to California in the gold rush. And didn't do badly."

He talks on and on. He is a big, well-built chap in whom the Irish ancestry is still apparent after four generations: red hair, rather dreamy eyes, a loud, contagious laugh, and naturally a name beginning with O', O'Mahoney or O'Shaughnessy or something of the sort. At each of the minute stops he demonstrates his counter. The melody of the cosmic rays in his headphones never ceases to enchant him. He is filled with enthusiasm when the crackle is louder at the top of the pass than it was in the valley. "Already more radioactivity," he explains. "Listen to the dance that's going on in there."

Toward noon we stop for half an hour in Silverton, an old mining town high up on a saddle. Tons of silver are said to have been hauled from here at one time. There is not much left of it. Only a miserable collection of corrugated iron houses, which we passed on the drive up, seems still to be inhabited. The waitress at the luncheon counter, which even at nearly ten thousand feet looks not very different from anywhere else in the States, informs us that the Anaconda people are now prospecting for tin and molybdenum. As she feeds the electric mixer and fries eggs for the guests on the electric hot plate, she can talk of nothing but the visit of a film company which recently filled the thin mountain air for several days with its noise and bustle.

"The whole place was in it," she reports. "We had to put on costumes of the gold-rush times and we got fifteen dollars a day as extras. There's a big picture of me in technicolor. Mr. Dailey, the star, fixed that with the producer because I gave him such good service." She empties the milkshake too quickly into my Irish friend's glass and spills a few drops. "Look out, Betty Grable," he warns her. Then he leaves a double tip.

As we wait for the bus to start we walk a few steps up and down Main Street. We see samples of rock on display. They are for sale to souvenir hunters—an assortment neatly tied with string to a cardboard mat. There is fire-red rock side by side with transparent crystal formations in shimmering violet, copper-green feldspar, dark mountain stone, dotted with hundreds of tiny gold flecks. Next to these one may see larger samples: whole fragments of quartz, feldspar, ilmenite. The man in the shop collects them himself. He is a lover of strange and beautiful minerals, such as exist up here on "America's hard backbone." When we ask him why he too has not joined the uranium hunters, he answers evasively, "I don't believe in it." More he apparently does not wish to say, although my companion presses him. "There," says the man and puts a new sample on the rubber mat with the Coca-Cola advertisement, "that's something for you: carnotite. Containing uranium. We used simply to throw the stuff away. Couldn't get anything for it. But now . . ." He makes an eloquent gesture.

Joe O'Something buys the bit of carnotite for half a dollar. It is covered with a poisonous-looking yellowish-green rash. "It's no beauty," he says as we stand in front of the bus which is beginning to fill, "but just listen." He holds his metal magician's wand to the stone, attends to the headphones with an air of rapture, then puts them over my head.

"Tock tick tock, tick tick, tock tock tock," they say quite loudly into my ear. That means, in the nervous rapping language of the earth spirits, as transmitted by the electronic tube in the Geiger counter: "Uranium, uranium, uranium."

"Down there," says the son of Ireland pointing in the direction of the bends in the road, "there's heaps of it."

And as the bus rolls downhill through tall glorious forests into the Rio Grande Valley, he keeps repeating, to the refrain of a song hit:

"Plenty, plenty and plenty."

The man of the Chamber of Commerce in Durango was rather worried. "We view all these newcomers with very mixed feelings," he says. "Our town has had a bad name for long enough. Every time I get to see my relations in the East it costs me an effort to say that I come from Durango. It used really to be pretty wild here.

The yellow-backed Westerns are still living on it. Durango is a name that sounds romantic. So the writers lay many of their stories in this place. Actually we cleaned up the worst saloons long ago and turned out the bad hats. We're a clean city. But now with the fairy tales about uranium all kinds of riffraff are coming in. They think they can bring back the Wild West ways again."

If you go by day through the main streets you see hardly any signs of Durango's rough past and few of the ostensible boom. The bars smell more strongly of fresh linoleum than of alcohol. If you speak of the uranium boom most people look blank. Yes, it seems one of the telephone-company inspectors has staked out a couple of claims in Montezuma County: hasn't grown rich on them yet. Else he would have given up his three-hundred-dollar job. And a druggist claims to have found a seam of pitchblende up on the plateau, but he was always a bit loony. The biggest money was made by a bright lad who sold Geiger counters to the treasure seekers. How about a beer?

So that is a theme on which the Durango people surprisingly do not care to dwell. Every word about it has to be dragged out of them. "Go to Dove Creek," I was advised; "there you'll find what you're looking for. Perhaps no uranium, but at least people who have nothing on their minds but that strange metal."

Mr. Genaro of Dove Creek, who gave me a lift on his truck up to the Colorado plateau, was not such a one. His communications were tuned to the same disappointing note I had heard, as soon as conversation turned to the new rush. He was of Italian origin, with strong shoulders and a steady self-confident gaze. Fifteen years ago fate had driven him to this remote corner of America, and he had no regrets.

As we drove along Highway 86 he pointed out the tilled fields and blossoming gardens to our right and left. He himself had bought such a plot of ground with a loan from the bank, had cleared and planted it and made it fruitful, and had obtained a good price in wartime for his products. "I found green gold," he laughed, "and more grows in my pocket at every harvest. Can you show me one of your treasure hunters who could put aside nearly a hundred thousand dollars in ten years and at the same time build up a property worth at least that much again?" he challenged. "But tell it to one of those loons and they shake their heads. That's not their line, the gentlemen say. Too much work. Too little profit. And all the while they worry themselves to death and can't ever sleep in peace at night. When I go out, the last thing, to smoke my good-night cigarette, I see the lights of the search lamps on the plateau. There they are, creeping about in the dark among the rocks, hacking and listening and gathering stone samples. And if once they really find something, they rush into debt to buy drills, dynamite, trucks and other equipment, on which they've got to keep paying until the boom is over, and there they are without a penny but with plenty of useless tools."

Once, the Italian said, he had invited an old miner, whose ability and energy he valued, to be his partner in clearing and preparing a new terrain. The old miner had only looked at him irritably, as at a stubborn child to whom the mother says he should not neglect his food for his play, and had not spoken to him again.

"Believe me," said the sturdy farmer, "it's not really the money they're after. They want adventure. They're looking for the miracle, the big surprise, the winning number. At bottom they're all vagabonds and gamblers."

But despite the contempt he had for his neighbors, their "frivolous way of life," as he called it, seemed to be running constantly in his thoughts. "Do you know what those guys imagine?" he asked just before he set me down. "That they're real men and we farmers nothing but sissies without energy, spunk or any fun in life. Morons!"

On the day of my arrival, the following paragraphs appeared in the *Dove Creek Press:* "The neighborhood is overrun by oil engineers, geologists, real-estate agents and uranium speculators. The representatives of private petroleum companies want to come in on the boom, but the sleuths of the government commission on atomic energy are also about to look mistrustfully over all those engaged in the mad rush for land with a mineral content."

This gold-rush atmosphere is nothing new for Dove Creek. The little settlement on the road to Utah has lived through more than one such upheaval, and more than one of the hangovers which follow it. The houses of Dove Creek, with their elegant false façades and pillared porticoes from which the white paint is flaking off, tell a tale of ascent and decline. One building still bears the sign, "Dove Creek Opera House." This dates from the Roaring Eighties or the Gay Nineties when Dove Creek, like every other large mining camp, acquired an opera house in which traveling companies occasionally presented operas, though far more frequently burlesque shows.

That was during the silver boom and the gold rush that followed it. Then came the radium fever and the vanadium "run." But in between lay years of poverty and oblivion. The treasure hunters left, the farmers and a few shopkeepers remained. And also the decaying evidences of brief splendor: gigantic bars with mirrors and full-bosomed beauties who continued to look down from the walls with the same vapid smile upon their now mainly four-legged admirers.

"Mr. Dove Creek," as the neighbors call the richest and best-known citizen, Matt Sitton, is a massive self-made man who has successfully survived the local ups and downs. The American newspapers call him the Uranium King, a title he wears with some diffidence. "I'm really rather a small man in the uranium business," he tells the visitor, whom he receives in the headquarters of the Dove Creek Bank, founded by himself and still smelling of fresh paint and damp cement. "The big boys are large firms like the Climax Corporation or the Vanadium Corporation of America, who have big business and the banks in the East behind them. They can put millions into the search for new metals and buy all the modern machinery which gives a profit margin. But an impersonal board of directors or of spectacled lawyers which looks after the interests of anonymous shareholders doesn't fit the idea of a uranium king. People want to imagine a tough guy who challenges luck with guts, energy and a bit of brutality. That had to be me."

Actually, Mr. Sitton, although his comfortable glass-enclosed office overlooks the high plateau with its "claims," has never pros-

pected in person for the elusive mineral. He, too, has merely
financed the men in the field and acquired through skillful investment what others sought for and occasionally found.

Originally Sitton came to the high Colorado plateau in search
of health, having suffered earlier from tuberculosis. This was at
the close of the First World War. The young man began as a village
schoolteacher, bought a small plot of land with his savings and
finally opened a shop in which treasure hunters could buy tools
and provisions.

That was the year of the radium boom. At the turn of the century
carnotite had been found locally, a mineral containing vanadium,
uranium and radium. The first pure radium had been extracted by
Madame Curie in 1898 from carnotite sent her by the French
scientists Poulot and Voileque, who had come across it in Paradise
Valley, near Dove Creek. It was not until the time of the First
World War that radium became commercially interesting because
of its use in the treatment of cancer and for phosphorescent watch
faces. Although the percentage of radium contained in the Colorado carnotite is infinitesimally small, its extraction, at a world-
market price of a hundred thousand dollars a gram, began to pay.

But in 1923 this house of cards fell. In the Congo, in-
comparably richer beds of uranium were discovered with a higher
percentage of pitchblende, and the Belgians brought radium onto
the world market at thirty thousand dollars less per gram. From
one day to the next the Dove Creek uranium diggers were out of
work. There was no further market for their carnotite. Many wan-
dered away from the region leaving their now worthless claims to
shopkeeper Sitton, as some sort of payment of their debts. Among
Mr. Sitton's debtors was an Irish priest by the name of O'Neill. He
had originally emigrated to America to earn funds for the building
of a church in his native village. But when he made several particularly promising finds the priest repeatedly postponed putting his
original intention into practice. Many inhabitants of Dove Creek
claim that this broken vow brought the misfortune of the radium
crisis upon them.

In any case, Mr. Sitton received from the priest on his deathbed the title to all his claims, with a last request that he assign at least a part of the possible profits to O'Neill's Irish parish. After a few years Sitton's patience began to bear fruit. First the steel industry required vanadium, likewise contained in carnotite, for hardening its products, and from 1942 onward the State began to buy carnotite for an unknown purpose. Only in 1945 did Sitton learn that the first atom bomb, exploded in Alamogordo, contained "his" uranium. A new era of undreamed-of prosperity with a sole insatiable buyer, the government, began for Sitton.

But although a neon sign now shines over Nick Cook's store "for articles of every kind," and Neil Bolt has built a house whose ground floor is let to a new liquor store; although Dove Creek, fertilized by the flow of money from speculators who are buying land left and right, grows out farther day by day into the rocky plateau, the natives do not believe in the duration of their luck, and if one of them happens to make a little money out of the boom, he buys, rather than a prospectable plot, a piece of farm land or some cattle. For even if their town looks as adventurous as a bit of scenery left over from a Wild West film, the regular inhabitants of Dove Creek are solid citizens who have no time for gambling and drinking—they know the end of the story better than the treasure seekers. They bet, like Mr. Genaro their fellow citizen, on the mild rather than the wild West, and gladly leave to Mr. Sitton his speculative celebrity.

The Sitton Group, reinforced by oil capital from Texas, controls the Colorado plateau to such an extent that the uranium seekers can hardly count on making further discoveries in the region of Dove Creek. So most of them soon move on westward into the neighboring state of Utah. This territory, once ruled by the Mormons, who were hostile to all mining, has withstood systematic penetration longer than any other tract of land in the Union. Particularly in southern Utah there are regions difficult of access where no white man has as yet set foot.

The search for uranium has been leading step by step to the opening of this nearly unexplored region. In a particularly jolt-proof type of jeep with special tires and independently driven rear wheels the uranium hunters venture into the trackless land, with its deep canyons and magically beautiful effects of light on petrified forests of reddish rock.

These gorges, separated from each other by wildly jagged mountain ranges, are so hard to reach that it would take years and years before single groups of treasure seekers could inspect them with Geiger counters. The American Government, wishing to speed up the acquisition at home of the ore indispensable to its atomic program, has provided airplanes equipped with instruments for the location from the air of promising uranium deposits.

The machine in which we flew from Monticello, Utah, had been transformed by the Atomic Energy Commission into a flying laboratory. Apart from the pilot and two technicians, we had with us Zerubabel S., one of the most experienced mineral hunters in the region. South of Dirty Brook he had sighted a hump which looked to him as though it contained uranium; but he had not been able to come close enough with his Geiger counter to verify his guess.

So there he sat in the cabin with an old-fashioned broad felt hat on his head, faded blue trousers, and an amulet fastened round his neck by a little silver chain, looking down at the wild, broken landscape of Utah while the technicians busied themselves with their implements. The day was exceptionally clear, and we flew so low as to be able plainly to see ruined huts, forsaken barracks, abandoned material: traces of the previous activities of the gold, silver and copper seekers. The old prospector knew the names of all these ghost towns. The bizarre rock statues hewn out by wind and water, looking like cathedral towers, Venetian bridges, human profiles or pyramids, seemed to make no impression on him, but he pointed out with excitement the species of wolflike wild dogs which roam these forlorn ravines without fear or hindrance.

But sharp as the eyes of the prospector were, the technicians of the A.E.C. did not rely upon them. After we had been flying about for ten minutes, Jones, the leading engineer, opened a floor trap and threw out a metal case attached to a cord about twenty yards long. In it was a vacuum tube hardly larger than a cigarette. "That's a magnetometer," Mr. Jones explained. "It has eyes sharper than a falcon's and sees through the surface rock down to the underground formations. The Navy used it during the war for detecting submarines. Here"—he pointed to a control dial—"it registers every alteration in the magnetic field."

In addition to this remarkable flying eye we had also brought with us a hypersensitive mechanical nose. An air valve at the head of the machine sniffed for the slightest traces of radon gas, which is emitted in minute quantities over beds of radioactive minerals. A Brown receiving apparatus could measure exactly how strongly the air samples were ionized by the gas and made this known through deflections on an electric dial. Finally our artificial ears were switched on. These consisted of a Geiger counter six times magnified, and protected by leaden slabs from the disturbing background noises of the cosmic rays. Listening into it we should be able to check on whether our "eye" and "nose" were telling the truth.

But before our mechanical spies had given notice of a discovery, the prospector called out: "There . . . it's over there." We circled above a mesa which bore an astounding resemblance to the dome of St. Peter's; the Geiger counter, now behaving as though it had a rattlesnake inside it, jerked the slate pencil bound to the magnetometer steeply upward on the graph paper and led the needle of the Brown recorder a frantic dance.

"I think you've got something there," said Jones and slapped the old prospector on the shoulder. "We'll look it over from close by in the next couple of days. With the helicopter we can get nearer than this, maybe even land."

Then he told the pilot to fly to Hanksville, the seat of one of the offices of the Atomic Energy Commission.

Over Hanksville lies a veil of silver dust. It is noon, and blazing hot, but the bulldozers know no siesta. They shovel and growl, run angrily against the obstacles that oppose them, finally thrust their way through them in a cloud of glittering splinters. The large roadbuilding machines roll in their wake. With their tall, almost perpendicular yellow cranes they look like powerful prehistoric animals advancing awkwardly with gigantic bodies erect.

A foreman in a crimson plastic helmet is giving orders into a microphone, which are amplified a hundredfold through a large loud-speaker. He stands there, legs apart, like an animal trainer in a circus and tells his performers which maneuvers to execute.

"Hey, Joe," he says, "thirty-five degrees! Slant this scraper more." Or: "Go on, Tuck, pull out the brute's teeth. Knock in the hook. Perhaps we can make it without dynamite."

A few months ago Hanksville was the most out-of-the-way hole in the most out-of-the-way corner of Utah. The hundred and fifty inhabitants lived chiefly on sheep raising. Quite by chance a tourist crossing the desert from San Rafael stopped here at "the end of the world." He was shown a crumbled house, formerly the residence of Butch Cassidy, Utah's most notorious desperado. With his Robbers' Roost Gang he held sway for years like a prince over the pathless hinterland. The inhabitants of Hanksville were his henchmen, who, for a share in Butch's loot, gave him and his boys board and lodging.

So in a few weeks' time there will be a broad highway to Hanksville. Even the dusty track to Hite, by the Colorado River, will be flattened out and widened. And a whole number of smaller roads lead into the Temple Mountains, to be followed only as far as road blocks with their warning notices that read, "No Entrance. Atomic Energy Commission."

In his makeshift office sits the branch manager of the A.E.C., a man aged, at most, thirty, who has all the appearance of a college graduate with his crew cut and his imposing horn-rimmed spectacles.

"Road building is almost as important as working the uranium," he tells the visitor. "For to get even a one-per-cent yield the rock containing the uranium must be taken away by the ton, and that's only possible over good roads. Quite a different thing from gold mining in the last century. Then a miner could usually wash out the gold sand alone or loosen the gold nuggets from the rock. The forty-niners and their followers didn't need much equipment apart from two or three pack mules and a gold-washing pan. Our uranium hunters need at least a truck, a jeep, diamond drills, pneumatic hammers and other mobile compressor apparatus, to get the bare minimum of results.

"Hey, Jack," he calls to a sunburned young man in an olive green sweatshirt who has been wiping a pair of dark glasses as he awaits his turn to speak to the boss, "take this gentleman over to Calamity Mine." Then, turning to me: "Don't worry, the 'calamity' is nothing to get upset about. The metal chasers of forty years ago hoped to find copper there and found only uranium! There are a couple of dozen 'calamity' mines in the neighborhood."

Before we leave, Jack gives his report in a few words. The trial drilling at hole 323 has not yet shown results, although a depth of 240 feet was reached. On the other hand, 317 seems to be developing favorably. Should blasting begin? The boss reflects a moment and asks whether the last test of 317 has yet been analyzed. Yes it had, on the spot, with scintillation counters and ionic chambers, but the laboratory's exact chemical analysis was not yet ready.

"Why don't we wait for it? Grand Junction will make hell hot for me if it finds out that I started blasting without a lab analysis. Okay?"

Would it be all right with me if we looked in at the lab on our way? Jack asks. The report might be ready. I gladly consent.

We cross the main street of Hanksville. Chickens and children with dirty noses are running about as untroubled as though the atomic age had never reached their village. In front of the houses sit old men and women, looking into the air and through the stranger.

The lab is in a new building hurriedly thrown together out of prefabricated parts. Over it a placard says, "The Rim of the World." Two young chemists and a lean geologist with shaven gray hair are just having their "coke," and pause as we come in.

With the "Say, you're taking it easy today," and the reply, "But *we* don't have time for sunbathing and pretty girls," the customary give-and-take is on. "What can we offer the gentleman?" asks the rather chubby chemist. "A blonde? Redhead? We have also a new brunette. . . ."

"Nonsense," says my guide, "you know I only care for yellowish-green and violet."

"Yeah," says the chemist, "he's got uranium, nothing but uranium, on the brain. Then, referring to your order of the nineteenth ultimo, what can we offer you? Hole 317? A hot little number. Here's the certificate, with best references. Great things can come of that number. Tell the chief."

Jack studies the paper handed to him, on which the exact percentages of the chemical analysis have been noted. "Looks good," he says, pleased.

But his boss is more difficult. To him the tests do not as yet indicate that hole 317 is productive. On the contrary, he fears they have fallen again on one of those confounded veins which simply break off after a couple of days. "No blasting, then?" asks Jack. "No . . . for the moment go on drilling," is the disappointing reply.

"There are three kinds of men here," says Jack as we bump in a jeep over the wide mule path to Calamity Mine, "the dreamers, the resigned and the disappointed."

I had asked him what types of men came out to Utah to find uranium. They were, he said, apart from the few old professional prospectors, nearly all fugitives. Fugitives from the boredom of modern cities and business offices. Fugitives who thought it less uncertain to go into desolate half-desert country than to stay on in the centers of civilization with the Damocles' sword of complete destruction hanging over them. But out here they generally found more offices, regulations, closed business hierarchies, into which they had to fit themselves. The West was no longer a place for the individualist. Naturally you could detach yourself and try to lead your own life, but you could do that also in the canyons of the big cities.

The chances of getting rich quick, through a lucky find, Jack held to be nonexistent. The soundings were far too irregular and

unsure for anything to be known about them until the whole complicated and expensive mechanism of trial drilling and continuous
laboratory verification had been set in motion. Should an individual
prospector ever make a find with his Geiger counter, he would
hardly have the means to exploit it alone. The best he could hope
for would be a small share from one of the big prospecting firms.
Naturally, after all expenses had been deducted the final balance
seldom showed much coming to him.

"I, too," Jack admitted, "hoped to go back to Illinois with my
pile. Now I've hired myself out instead as liaison man between the
A.E.C. and the Utah Mining Corporation. As jobs go, it's not bad.
Sometimes a bit lonely with no girls or entertainment. It's only after
you've lived out here for a few months that you appreciate city
life."

Despite all his frankness Jack had not yet spoken to me on the
topic that causes the greatest worry to private promoters
and government enterprise alike: the protection of the health of
the men who deal with the radioactive ore.

When we arrived at Calamity Mine (a primitive shaft neither
well propped up nor properly ventilated) work had come to a
standstill. The miners had collected round a colleague, who had
fainted in the mine and been brought with all haste to the surface.

"Radium poisoning," they were saying, "the yellow sickness."

"These miners are unteachable," complained Jack. "They refuse to understand that this stuff is different from coal or whatever
other mineral they've mined before. We've tried to educate them:
so far without success. They claim our carnotite has so little uranium in it that a miner would die of old age before he could get a
big enough dose of radioactivity to hurt him. An accident like this
may teach them to work in their protective suits and use their air
filters."

Under the circumstances a closer view of the mine was out of
the question. We quickly brought the sick man back to Hanksville, where I had to take leave of Jack and his boss.

But this was curious: although on the earlier part of my journey through the uranium country I had not heard the "yellow disease" so much as mentioned, I now ran across it nearly everywhere. In the little town of Nucla I heard of a man called Frank Wilson who, after holding a job in a uranium refinery, developed ulcers on his hands and feet and finally died. In Uravan, where there is a mill for processing uranium ore, they spoke of a farmer who had sued because his cattle, whose pasture lay near the establishment, had been dying off of an inexplicable disease. In Naturita, where another refinery is being operated, an engineer was obliged to give up his post on account of being seized with cramps whenever he handled radioactive material.

And in Durango, where everyone had been struck dumb the week before, whenever I asked about the uranium rush, all mouths opened without resistance, as soon as I touched upon the theme of radium poisoning.

"Now perhaps you see why we're not pleased with all this," said a businessman who, on my first visit, had refused to enter into a discussion of uranium. "Now try driving just outside the town. Take the extension of Main Street to the south. Then you'll understand even better."

I did not have to go far on foot to realize what he meant. About three quarters of a mile beyond the town I suddenly saw the familiar yellow-green of carnotite on the leaves of a tree. A few steps more and I stood before a remarkable meadow. I should say: a former meadow. Now it looked more like a ghosts' dance floor full of pale blades of grass, dry as paper, which crumbled at the touch into a poisonous-looking dust. My jacket and shoes were already coated with the same yellow-green substance and the farther I went, the more thickly was everything around me—the withered trees, the fields, the telegraph wires, even the advertisement posters—coated with this repulsive powder. It must have been in my hair, on the skin of my face. I imagined I tasted something bitter on my lips after wandering a mile through this death-stricken region.

Suddenly I found myself standing before a gate with a warning sign:

"STOP! This is the Private Property of the Vanadium Corporation of America (V.C.A.)."

In the distance I heard the creaking of mechanical mixers. Vapors floated from a longish hall: their color was also greenish yellow. A uniformed policeman saw me and barked, without my having asked him anything: "No workers taken on here. Go to the town office."

Later, at the central office of the Atomic Energy Commission in Grand Junction, when I asked about the radium illness, I was told: "We are aware of the facts and intend to issue strict protective regulations." As evidence I was shown the newly published report by P. W. Jacoe, the head of an investigating committee, which read:

> Employees of mines and factories which produce or refine uranium ore suffer from radium poisoning and silicosis. They do not appreciate the danger of radioactive rays because they cannot see them. Chemists touch refined uranium with their bare hands. Laborers eat their lunches in workrooms which have become radioactive. No regular medical inspections are made of employees, who will perhaps feel only after many years the effects of their present occupation in the inadequately protected works of the V.C.A. in the form of blood diseases, bone degeneration and possible cancer.

Since, however, little or nothing is said of this side of the uranium rush, more and more fortune hunters pour into Utah and Colorado, in search of something which has become rarer in America than rare metals: they come in search of adventure, and they keep coming and coming.

A TOWN MUST DIE—A TOWN MUST GROW

Augusta, Georgia

AMERICAN SMALL TOWNS nearly always suffer from patriotic mega-lomania. To induce motorists to make a short stop, the Chamber of Commerce will announce on large posters at the entrance to the town that this is the Salad Capital of the World or America's Artichoke Metropolis or, briefly and simply, the Most Beautiful Place on God's Earth.

I came across self-praise of a similar and yet very different kind at the entrance to Ellenton, one of the first places beyond the border from Georgia into South Carolina. But this time there was no advertising tablet set up in shining colors, no slogan calling attention to itself in flickering neon tubes, but four clumsy boards on which an anonymous person had written in an awkward hand:

> *It is hard to*
> *Understand why*
> *Our town*
> *Must be destroyed*
> *To make a bomb*
> *To destroy*
> *Someone else's town*
> *That he loves just the same*
> *As we do ours—*
> *We think they found*
> *Not only the best spot in the U.S.A.*
> *But in the whole world.*

We love the dear hearts
And friendly people
Who live in our town.

That Ellenton is not only the best spot in the U.S.A. but also in the whole world is a fact only recently known to its inhabitants. Formerly they considered themselves less lucky to live in this sparse pine land. They swore at the hard climate, the cotton borer which made the lean harvests still leaner, the sandy red soil, the swampy lowlands on the Savannah River and their own history which seemed to condemn them to a life apart from progress. They have sung their melancholy little song to whoever wished—or did not wish—to listen (in particular the tax collector), with its closing couplet:

Land and people both are poor.
If they don't steal, how will they endure?

Only when the little town had been condemned to death, only when it became clear that nothing—nothing on earth—could save it and its four neighboring towns, did the inhabitants of Ellenton begin to mourn as for a close relative whose worth one recognizes only when the doctor has given him up.

The voice which informed Ellenton of its imminent doom came over the wireless on the twelve o'clock news on November 18, 1950. It was the indifferent voice of an announcer, a voice without anger and without any trace of sympathy. The townships of Ellenton, Dunbarton, Jackson, Bush and Meyers Mill would be evacuated within a measurable space of time and the ground leveled, it was stated, to make room for a new complex of atomic factories. This was reported with complete objectivity, for nowadays the curse that falls on men and their possessions often takes the concise, dispassionate form of the telegram: instead of the angel with the flaming sword there presently appears to those stricken a friendly gentleman from Washington who patiently bends his ear to the despairing with unflinching equanimity.

For even though Mr. Nelson—the name of the bearer of ill tidings in the present case—derived his authority merely from government offices in the American capital, he was as deaf to entreaties as a heavenly messenger bringing notice of doom who is begged for pardon or postponement. Almost as soon as the project was known his attention was drawn, at an open meeting in the overcrowded schoolhouse, to the fact that many families of Ellenton and its surroundings had lived here for generations and could not change their residence as lightly as city folk. Why, they wanted to know, could not the government find an unsettled, uncultivated tract of earth in the whole of America on which to build its atomic factory? But he had all his answers pat, this messenger. He even showed sympathy, made wary promises, but the decision itself was no longer subject to change.

So the inhabitants of Ellenton now sit in the Busy Bee Café, one of those frankly uncared-for wooden barracks whose broken windowpanes have long been replaced temporarily with cardboard. Temporarily? No, now finally and forever. In a few months the Busy Bee will consist of a few splinters of wood, just like Mike Cassel's "Long Store," just like the Baptist Church, the poolroom and Ellenton's single "historical house" where the arbitrary arrest of two Negroes in 1876 led to a bloody and mortal clash between blacks and whites. They are waiting only for the large yellow bulldozers which will knock down their homes and shops with two or three thrusts, for the heavy road-building machines that are already rolling in this direction from North Augusta, beating down trees before them, shoveling away entire hillocks. They are waiting for the great rollers which flatten everything that has not yet been evened out, and will turn a living natural landscape into a sterile industrial one.

Only the little railway station will be preserved from destruction, even considerably enlarged, it is said, in order to be able to handle the consignments of material for the new factory. It, too, is over a hundred years old, one of the first stops on the steam railway introduced by a few wealthy gentlemen in a speculative frame of mind earlier into South Carolina than into other, far more thickly populated, parts of the United States. With it the industrial era entered this region. Therefore it alone may survive the coming of the new industry. The smoke-spitting "fire steeds" were greeted as unwillingly as the atomic factory is now, and several of the neighboring planters ordered their slaves to stand in the road of the foreign monster and hold it up. But soon they renounced these demonstrations and chose instead to buy shares in the line.

The Ellenton men wait and wait. They play the endless games of cards, uninterrupted by any work, of which they have often dreamed; for there is no longer any point in lifting a finger. The government has promised to compensate the farmers for their work up to the time of demolition. But who wants to drudge for a harvest he will never gather? Even if someone were to put cash down on the table for unripe fruit and cotton that will never flower, who wants that sort of cash?

They propose, in any case, to present the gentlemen in Washington with bills the latter will consider too high. In the pauses between games of gin rummy, damages are calculated. They play for a tenth of a penny but think in thousand-dollar bills, seldom if ever seen, which they would like to collect from the government.

"Yes, but with all the dollars in Washington, I can't buy hunting land like ours," says a lanky redhead who owns a sawmill, the only factory in the town, and will open a similar one over in Georgia. "I'll have to sell the dogs, too. The city's no place for them. What's to make up for that sort of thing?" The other men nod, the cards are dealt, the next hand played in silence.

Conversation at the Busy Bee or round the iron stove in Mike Cassel's Long Store might be expected to turn on the bombs for which explosive material is soon to be produced here. But some sort of inhibition prevents the men from alluding to this topic. The uppermost theme is whether any government has a right to expel free men from their plot of earth; "especially in peacetime," emphasizes one of them. "When they built Oak Ridge there was a war on and, even so, plenty of farmers refused to get out till they had the burning logs pulled out of their fireplaces."

"This time it's not a real peace," he is told in reply, "else we would have put up a fight." At first Ellenton started taking up a collection to pay for a lawyer in Washington, a lobbyist who might be able to reverse the government's decisions. But Mike Cassel, whose opinion carries great weight, opposed the project. It was no use, he considered, and would only make bad blood. "We're powerless when it comes to such big decisions," he said. "If only I knew why just our particular place should be so valuable and indispensable. Our fathers would have fought for this ground but we're helpless."

Most concise was the answer given to a stranger offering patriotic comfort on the ground of "history is being made": "To hell with history!"

Meanwhile, more strangers come daily. Mainly the curious or the covetous. The curious have read of Ellenton's fate in the newspapers. Most of them go away disappointed, seeing nothing sensational in the everyday life of the small town. The covetous wish to do business. One of them, a house mover, has come in haste from California, rightly scenting an interest in his services. He offers anyone willing to pay the price the transport of his house lifted from its foundations, as it stands, to anywhere outside the new government reserve. To those for whom this operation is too expensive there are available the services of a photographer who will quickly take a likeness of the home before its destruction.

These two business people with their noses for the main chance are not doing badly. On the other hand, the casual laborers, who started arriving in their jalopies on the second day after the news had broken and asking where to apply for the four-dollar-an-hour wage for moving the graveyards, have been disappointed. Only one dollar an hour was being offered, and at that price none but the Negroes in the vicinity of Ellenton wanted the work.

These, however, are busy from five in the morning until dark. The government has allowed each person to remove his dead before the wall of the atomic reservation closes round the whole territory. And since the state is paying, everyone, even if he has not visited any of the cemeteries in years, wishes to profit by the offer, only to take advantage of the public coffers. No one in or about Ellenton had imagined that the dead neighbors were more numerous than the living ones. "What a crowd!" cry the grave-diggers with ever-renewed astonishment. "Thousands and thousands." And they no doubt think: "How many dollars will that mean to us?"

The hundred-odd burial grounds of Ellenton, Dunbarton, Jackson and the surrounding area are thus being systematically uprooted, generation by generation. Each day Army trucks drive north with the bones packed into fresh pine coffins. On their way they encounter with increasing frequency mechanical shovels, bulldozers and other combined earth-shaking machines. These monsters are often so large that they cannot give way. The dead must wait at the edge of the road until they finally have free passage.

The citizens of Augusta, about twenty-five miles from Ellenton, greeted the news of the large atomic project with scarcely concealed enthusiasm. If Ellenton people went to Augusta on business, they returned at night, angry and bitter, to their doomed little town. Their neighbors' loud rejoicing over the future hurt them deeply. "If one of the Augies sees me," remarks someone between two deals in Ellenton, "he acts at first as if he were sorry. 'Too bad about you folks,' he'll say. But as soon as we get talking he begins on the big business, the opportunity of a lifetime that's waiting for Augusta, and by the time we separate he's forgotten that the boom they're waiting for wouldn't be possible without our hard luck."

That is the way they spoke in the beginning, when the vanguard of the great foreign invasion had reached Augusta, the handful of engineers, architects and government officials who were to prepare the ground. When I visited the town six months later the mood had changed. The inhabitants of Augusta were often at a loss to know whether to rejoice or to curse at the new development.

"Life used to be so pleasant here," complained the old-established Augies. "We were at home in a quiet, friendly, distinguished town. There was room for everyone. If you wanted to go shopping you could park wherever you liked. If you decided to eat out of an evening there were enough tables to be had in the restaurants. Naturally guests were hospitably greeted and decently served.

Everyone knew everybody else. People could stand still in the street and have a chat. But now?"

"Now," answers Mr. Lester S. Moody of the Chamber of Commerce, "now you earn more than you ever did in your life. Augusta is on the way to becoming a metropolis with the highest average income in Georgia. Now we're getting new blood from other states, young enterprising people from all over the country. The building of a large atomic factory in the Ellenton district means as much to us as if we'd brought fifty normal enterprises to Augusta all at the same time."

Mr. Moody is rightly a trifle put out when he hears so many critical voices among his fellow citizens. He feels himself rightly responsible for the boom which has so completely altered Augusta's life. For years he made propaganda, through petitions and trips to Washington, for the building of a dam on the Savannah River, and finally, with the help of influential Georgians in the Senate and the House of Representatives, pushed through the "Clark Project" not far from Augusta. And again, because this power station already existed, the Atomic Energy Commission had been able to plan the big establishment for the production of tritium in the region.

And now he gets no thanks!

In the evening, Broad Street, Augusta's main thoroughfare, is far too narrow for all the cars and people. From the corner of First Street to Seventh is a good twenty-minutes' drive. The pavements are crowded with the young recruits from a neighboring Army camp; the cheaply and loudly dressed womenfolk of the newcomers who, to the disgust of the old residents, do their shopping in slacks; and the building workers or dynamiters who are blasting or erecting steel scaffolding on the site of the forthcoming atomic establishment. They wear their aluminum helmets even after work and stare as shamelessly at the women as at the young girls who, with their damp hair in curlers, are running some last-minute errand before the beginning of night with its new and exciting entertainments.

For the old-fashioned and rather prudish city is beginning to paint her unpretentious face with neon lights and to frolic wildly at a late hour. Quite suddenly night life has come to Augusta. Unpretentious little taverns transform themselves into dance halls and bars, larger establishments engage entertainers. The voices of blues singers, magnified by the microphone, are audible in the streets, together with their guitar accompaniment.

When Mr. Moody pleaded in the Capitol for the new dam, he wished to start a "chain reaction." For where there is electric current and a good water supply, new manufacturing enterprises will soon settle, bringing with them workers from the vicinity and from farther afield. Each new industrial worker, as American experience has shown, brings five to six people along with him into a city. That is, apart from his own family, a complete outfit of officials, business people and artisans who again bring along their own families and their own requirements.

Thus the opening of a new factory with three thousand workers may mean the influx of about twenty thousand people. But now in several months thirty-six thousand workers have streamed into Augusta, with thousands and thousands in their wake, so that suddenly, a population of seventy thousand has been more than trebled. Augusta has become a boom town. And under this assault, Mr. Moody's chain reaction has no means of keeping the social powers of explosion within bounds.

When the citizens of Ellenton now come to Augusta the Augies complain of their lot. "It's as if a bomb had hit our town," they say. "This chaos, this dreadful confusion, this lack of peace. . . ."

All the Ellenton people can do is to smirk maliciously.

The tavern posters say: "Unaccompanied ladies must leave this place unaccompanied." But nobody has time to check up on whether this police regulation is being carried out. Now and then single girls are arrested as suspected prostitutes. They are examined and taken to the bus with a one-way ticket in their pockets. A few hours later they are back in Augusta.

In the hospital there are not enough beds even for the births.

There are too few doctors in the place, too few police and too few street cleaners. There is too little of all and everything. At certain hours a place in the crowded cocktail bar of the biggest hotel costs a dollar's "rent." The shops stay open till eleven at night and even so are crowded to bursting at nearly every hour. Sometimes a shop will suddenly close during working hours and hang out the information "Our employees must rest for a few minutes." If you want to have your clothes laundered you must wait from two to three weeks and be grateful for having them accepted at all. The movie theaters play day and night without interruption. Even between midnight and six in the morning the houses are well filled. The same single bedroom is often inhabited day and night by different occupants, sleeping and working at different times. Some of these "hot beds" are said to be used in three shifts.

The Municipal Council could relax the situation by permitting the establishment of new hotels and businesses and the immigration of men of every trade. But it seldom grants licenses. Only a very small number of newcomers can reckon on settling here permanently. "We want no doubtful enterprises or people," is the argument. An old-established businessman reasons more honestly: "Why should we share the shower of gold with outsiders? After all, we've got to take plenty of inconvenience into the bargain."

In Augusta's gloomy town hall the city fathers defend themselves against the accusation of doing nothing to stem this flood of people. The personnel of the atomic factory would eventually amount to only six thousand men, they argue. That would mean, including their families and essential followers, an increase in population of approximately forty thousand. But all the other workers with their adherents, whom one still saw in Augusta, would leave as soon as the new streets, highways and factory buildings were completed. These temporary guests could therefore not be considered in planning the future. One had to make shift, in the meantime, as best one could. The permanent residents of Augusta should tell themselves that the unpleasant accompaniments of the boom would soon disappear.

But in the meantime where are the newcomers to lodge? What is to be done with them? Augusta, comes the answer, is not the only town near the Savannah Project (as the new factory is called, with the little word "atomic" carefully omitted). Aiken, for instance, is much nearer the building area and has a duty too.

But in Aiken the attitude to the new arrivals and to the whole "damned project" is still more hostile. This idyllic little city, with its shady streets of hard-packed red earth, its residential quarters and magnolia gardens, is candidly afraid of "all those people" who have recently poured into the region. To Aiken the large racing stables of the East are in the habit of sending their stock for a winter's fodder rest. Aiken is a highly exclusive "horseman's town" whose elegant clubhouses on Whisky Road await the annual rendez-vous of the racing people from all over America. Now, into this social Southern atmosphere of fox hunting, hunt balls and garden parties, the *newest world* threatens to intrude with all its noise, ugli-ness and brutal dynamism. This is not tolerable. Aiken is prepared at most to concede the purchase or building of villas to a few gentlemen at the top of the administrative hierarchy. The uncouth workers, when they come, are courteously told: "So sorry."

Where, then, will they dwell, the thousands and thousands of newcomers who have found no accommodation in Augusta or Aiken? I came upon them where so much in America that is un-finished and in the making can be found: at the edge of the town, in a no man's land between town frontiers. Here there are no munici-pal taxes to be paid, but neither are there usually any police. And no carting of rubbish. And naturally, no schools for the chidren. I found them in "trailer camps," the inevitable accompaniment of every boom. These are the temporary settlements of people to whom uprooting no longer means pain and separation as it does to those of Ellenton, but has become a normal way of life. The people who live here have understood the law of the age, this age of mass migrations. They have bought themselves a house they can pull along with them on the great treks, a house on wheels, a trailer.

America has always been on the move. In 1940 this roving, which had somewhat abated after the turn of the century, received a fresh impetus. Much of the armament industry was transferred to sparsely settled regions. From the great centers of the East the migratory movement pushed increasingly to the South and West. From the great road and rail junctions thrown like a loose net over the broad continent, it branched off into the fallow territories that remained within the net's wide meshes.

And the trailer, the movable house, is the type of dwelling which best meets the requirements of the uprooted man. He simply hooks it onto the car and drives his entire family wherever there happens to be paying work. This sounds like a pleasant life for happy vagabonds. Actually it is not quite so carefree. The trailers may not pull up at will at the edge of the road, in the woods or by the sea, but must keep to regulations which require that for every halt involving more than a brief rest they park in "trailer camps."

Such caravan camps have now been set up over the whole vicinity of the atomic project near Ellenton. They form themselves around parking places for whose use a weekly rent is paid to the owner. Often, though by no means always, the movable house can be linked in these places to the public utilities: to water, electric light, sewerage, all hastily laid on with no pretense of durability.

Before the Second World War the owners of houses on wheels considered themselves an elite. Their existence was filled with an air of adventure. Sometimes they followed their pleasure and the sun. Not infrequently they fled before the tax collector or the police. Absolved from civil regularity, gypsies with comfort, they saw themselves as the real descendants of the founding generations who had traveled West in the slow covered wagons.

But the Second World War with its mass displacement of soldiers and workers altered the role of the trailer. It was an object no longer of luxury but of utility, a necessity for a family wishing to follow its father into a garrison area or a place of work with no housing accommodation. If the earlier, voluntary "trailerites" found their cramped quarters romantic, the new enforced nomads stress the disadvantages of their way of life.

Besides, the trailer camps have lost their original character. Once they were resting and camping places in which a jolly company of wanderers and vagabonds held sway, now they might be described as improvised industrial slums. Such a camp, one of the two-hundred-odd dotting the surroundings of the hydrogen bomb factory under construction, is Green View, situated on the bank of the Savannah in the meager shade of a few pines.

The hundred and twenty inhabitants casually gathered here have been on the move for many years. The men have worked as riveters, pipe layers, cement mixers, truck drivers, in just about all of the forty-eight states. In Oklahoma and Arkansas they laid a section of the natural-gas main which will connect north Texas with Massachusetts. They built the new barracks of the Chemical Warfare Center in Maryland in record time and filled the wire scaffolding of the Friant Dam in California with concrete. A few of the trailerites are even planning a trip to Alaska by the new highway, which one of them helped to construct during the war. The long journey might well pay, for up there, where gigantic flying fields are being built, the wages are at least double those in the United States.

While the men work over there on the new atomic factory, the Green View women wash their linen, strike up temporary friendships with temporary neighbors and rail in chorus against the owner of the camp who puts in an appearance only to collect the weekly five dollars a stand but has still done nothing about getting the leaky shower pipe repaired. The radios are turned on all day long and fill the solitude of Green View with the heart-rending dialogues of the soap operas, the latest musical hits and advertisements for washing materials, liver pills and every form of household patent, the "gadget" dear to America.

The trailerites' living quarters are crammed with gadgets. The men have been earning well for years and the mobile working groups' standard of living has been constantly rising. Anything that is "portable"—that can be taken in small space on endless journeys—may be found in the trailers, themselves portable homes. In nearly every portable home there are portable phonographs and sewing machines, there are little folding chairs, and tables that can shrink to the shape of a furled umbrella. The clothes hang in a transparent collapsible cupboard-substitute, the children play with enormous blown-up rubber animals which will be deflated at night into sad flabby rags. In front of one of the oblong carriages there is even a portable "radar grill" which fries steaks with "atomic speed."

When, a few days ago, a police patrol came over from Augusta and claimed that two of the families parking in Green View were Negro, the cops were energetically repelled. They should concern themselves with other things, they were told. What about first catching the scoundrel who attacked little Lynn Morgan in the trees over there three weeks ago, or arresting the thief who stole Mrs. Mulligan's washing from the line?

At this the policemen retired from no man's land, leaving the trailerites behind with their semicircle of cars round the camp, their improvised porches and their view over the meager greenery: though not without threatening to see to it that the Northerners would fall in with the customs of the hospitable South. But before they take further measures to enforce the racial separation obligatory in Georgia, there will be nothing left of the camp but a heap of refuse, of old paper and rusty tins. The residents of Green View will again be strewn to the four winds. To Florida and Oregon, to North Dakota and Pennsylvania, to every place where factories, dams and military establishments are being built.

THE PLACE MARKED "SECRET"

Santa Fe, New Mexico

THE GATEKEEPER has sharp eyes. He must have seen my Santa Fe driver hundreds of times but he gives no sign of recognition. No friendly "Hello" such as people exchange in America when they have hardly, or never, met, no smile, no greeting. A glance at the identity card sealed into an artificial material, another at the special stamped permit fixed above the car's license plate, a correct nod of the head, and now he takes the letter designed to bring about my admission to Los Alamos. He reads it very slowly, very attentively, although the contents are a standard form for all invitations to outsiders into the atomic city. A nod. Without looking at me the custodian goes into his spick-and-span glass cage at the side of entrance track number four. I see him take up the telephone receiver, speak into it, then wait, this time staring at me sharply through the window. He stands there quietly, with no trace of impatience. A gigantic fellow in a cowboy hat and a light blue shirt on which a lightning flash and the initials of the Atomic Energy Commission, A.E.C., are stamped. His trousers are carefully folded over and their ends stuck into heavy leather boots.

So this is how a city gate looks in the second half of the twentieth century. The broad road climbing in many twists and turns out of the Rio Grande Valley has suddenly widened into a circle and athwart it stands a modern rectangular granite structure, a flat-roofed traffic sluice, which conducts the stream of automobiles into six small canals, flanked by a watchtower such as one also finds at the entrance to prisons and concentration camps. Through the window of the car I see, to the right and left of it, the city wall. Not a wall of stone or earth but a high, broad-meshed wire netting which could hardly resist a good pair of garden shears but is sure to be protected by photoelectric cells and an alarm system. Above it, very long thin pylons with lamps that seem like pinheads which, at the fall of darkness, set up a floodlight barrier of glaring white rays.

Never has there been anything like it in America. It is as though the country without castles, moats and drawbridges were making up for its lack of Middle Ages: a town of ten thousand inhabitants behind a wall protected by electric eyes. No one can come here uninvited, no one leave without notice.

I try to get out and stretch my legs. One of the blue-shirted cowboys with a friendly smile gestures: stay inside. So I lean as far as possible out of the open window. By now six or seven other cars are waiting behind us. In the neighboring lanes the traffic is also blocked. But no one is impatient, no one grumbles. The drivers sit at their wheels and stare into space as if they were half asleep.

How often in America have I seen this look of resignation, this patience; on soldiers standing in the "chow line," on men and women queueing silently before theater box offices, on New York motorists on a Sunday evening wedged front and back between other cars waiting for hours to be able to move. No joking, no swearing, hardly a sound except for the turning of the motors is audible here at the gate to Los Alamos. It is early morning, but the August sun already burns down from a clear sky onto the freshly tarred road. On the other side of the barbed-wire division a gray bus has driven up. Men and women quickly get out. They speak loudly, call to one another, press against the exit barrier. They are Indians from one of the neighboring pueblos returning from work in the "forbidden city." In their shabby overalls, their loudly checked shirts, with huntsmen's or mechanics' caps and sunglasses, they are scarcely recognizable as the original inhabitants of this land. Only by the careless way in which they wear the working uniform of our time—by a wreath of light-blue and pink beads hanging over a faded jersey—does one gather that they have not been altogether assimilated into the standardized mold of the white majority.

The Indians are quickly disposed of. But we continue to wait. That seems to annoy my driver. As the workmen, now on our side, climb into their bus, again laughing loudly, he angrily presses the hooter.

At first this produces the effect of someone's letting fall an indecent word in a drawing room. Shocked faces look out of the windows of all the cars. "That isn't done," they seem to say. But already a second, a third, a fourth have copied us and honked their horns. And the echo rolls on. Six, eight, twelve and still more hooters say what the tongues did not think worth expressing. Is it merely an eruption of strained nerves? Is it indignation at this sort of road control, unfamiliar in the "land of the free"? Or is it simply the pleasure of noise? Even the armed attendant on the watchtower balcony looks down in some surprise at the wave of sound surging up to him. He does not take the little revolt seriously, but grins all over his face. Our controller is in less of a mood for humor. Without a word he approaches us. Without a word he hands me back my letter and with it a cold celluloid-like brooch with a serial number which shows me to be a transitory visitor and must always be worn visibly on the lapel of the coat. With an irritable motion of the hand he signs us to drive on.

"I'd like to know who those guys think they are," my driver grumbles good-humoredly; "as if we didn't pay taxes for them." And with that we rolled into Los Alamos.

There are few cities so impressive from afar as Los Alamos. A gigantic flat block of stone, which from a distance looks nearly rectangular, pushes its narrow side forward into the Rio Grande Valley. On this high natural pedestal whose walls, in many places nearly perpendicular, slope off into deep small canyons, the few buildings visible from below appear small and even fragile. European scientists working up here have remarked that this was how they had pictured the castle of the Grail seen from a distance. One could indeed imagine, approaching from Santa Fe, that there was a castle or monastery on the ridge of the mesa, did not the silvery claws of smoke from the laboratory building soon destroy the illusion.

The entrance road, beginning behind the wall of Los Alamos, returns the visitor almost brutally to the present. East Road, as it is called, is bordered on both sides by the usual American suburban sights. The pale-green prefabricated houses presumably originate from the same enterprise which sets up similar colonies in the neighborhood of Detroit, Gary and Pittsburgh. Neither the trailer settlement nor the heaps of building material on the side of the road are lacking. The laboratory building one has seen from afar could just as well belong to a linoleum or zipper factory. From the outside it is as unassuming and unostentatious as a cardboard box.

How many such laboratories Los Alamos possesses and where they are situated only the initiated know. From the map given to visitors more than half are missing: the whole thickly built technical region is just a white space. Naturally this "tech area," which also extends into other mesas divided by deep narrow canyons, is separated from the rest of the settlement by heavily reinforced wire fences, and within this reserve there are again regions to which only certain persons have access. And inside some of the buildings, specific floors or even single suites or rooms are separately guarded. They may be entered only by the selectest of the select. Thus lattice closes around lattice, wall around wall, control post follows upon control post. Every tenth inhabitant belongs to the security division, and is one of the thousand persons exclusively occupied with the control and protection of the settlement.

A man eligible for entry into more than one of the sections marked with different numerals, and shut off one from the other, possesses the requisite number of identity cards, each bearing a different numeral. For a time in atomic-town society, which leaned toward an occupational caste system, the "many numbered" were looked upon as an elite. Some, in their pride of rank, took to wearing their accumulated numerals like orders upon their breast. This pride had a fall when it transpired that a manual laborer doing unskilled repair jobs now in this section, now in that, was parading more numerals across his chest than anyone in town, while the state manager, with the function of mayor, was a humble three-number man. So that form of snobbery suddenly ended.

Even in the residential district of Los Alamos, with its houses, shops, churches, schools and hospitals like those of any other town, a passing visitor from "down below" may not move about unsupervised. My constant companion, into whose sure hands I was entrusted upon leaving the car, was Mr. S. of the Public Information Office, a talkative, jovial gentleman with a round rosy face patterned with the tiny veins of a drinker. For reasons which he did not clarify he had changed over from a large New York advertising firm to Los Alamos which he, like all residents of the atomic town, refers to as "the Hill."

Mr. S. did his best to make the Hill, in my eyes, a high peak of social development. Not only was the climate up here "the healthiest compared with that of any industrial settlement of an equivalent size" but all other conditions of life were perfect to a Utopian degree. Here there were neither rich nor poor, only well-paid citizens entitled to a pension and drawing their government salaries at regular monthly intervals. Since the taking up of an appointment depended on the Atomic Energy Commission, there could be no idle or unemployed in Los Alamos. "We have the highest average income of any community of ten thousand or over in the United States and are the only good-sized town without crime," Mr. S. announced. "Anyone who moves up here is carefully tested before and during his stay for his capacities and reliability. The moral standard of the population is therefore exceptionally high. We have, moreover, the population with the highest intelligence quotient in America because the laboratories employ so many academic and highly qualified special workers."

It would not have needed all these superlatives to show me that Los Alamos is a quite exceptional place. Actually, this walled settlement on a plateau three thousand feet high should not be called a town at all. For any town must have a certain proportion of freedom in order to be able to develop and live, even to be able to die. But the collection of houses and workshops on the Hill above the Rio Grande is an artificial and arbitrary product. It will never be anybody's home because no right of permanent residence may be acquired and the whole population is looked upon as transient. If a man gives up his job, if he is discharged or pensioned, he must also give up his house, which belongs to the government, and leave Los Alamos. For this reason one sees no old people on the Hill, with the exception of a very few indispensable scientific pundits. Should a person lose his usefulness to his employer the state, by reason of his age, and be replaced by a younger man, he has no further claim on the scanty living space of the atomic town. The many children, whom I watched in the streets playing a modern version of hopscotch in which the chalked squares to be jumped had "radioactive" or "contaminated" written on them, will, when they reach the working age, have to find an occupation in Los Alamos or else leave. If the work in the laboratories or other licensed enterprises does not appeal to them, or if they fail to pass the security department's personality and aptitude tests, there is no staying on in the town where they were born and reared.

So the people working in Los Alamos never lose the sense of impermanence. Their dissatisfaction is most apparent in their criticisms of "Zia," a building society named after the Indian sun goddess, which, through the Atomic Energy Commission, has built and furnished houses on government land against fixed payment, and now administers them. Zia was long reproached with building too slowly and too little. Hardly were there signs of relief of the housing shortage when the complaints began to turn on poor upkeep and a "dictatorship of taste." The case of the electric plug is typical. A number of tenants asked for the removal of an ugly plug attached just over the imitation fireplace in the living room. The request was denied. It turned out that a director of Zia, living in Los Alamos, wanted such a wall socket for an electric clock standing on his mantelpiece. Therefore it had also to be installed in all the other houses, and it had to stay.

For lunch, Mr. S. took me to "the oldest building in Los Alamos," Fuller Lodge, a former boarding school built of heavy square-hewn stones. For until 1942 there was nothing on the mesa but Colonel Conell's exclusive educational institution. The colonel protested until the day of his death against the government's appropriation of the Hill and never found out for what purpose it was taken over. During the first two years of Los Alamos nobody was given so much as a hint as to who was working up there and on what project. The atomic scientists gave their address as Post-Office Box 1593, Santa Fe. In official memoranda Los Alamos was referred to as "Terrain Y" and the news service cooperated by scattering false rumors in the neighborhood regarding the nature of the work being carried on.

At present, guests, such as congressional delegates and scientific consultants invited to Los Alamos for a few days or weeks, are lodged in the schoolboys' rustic, wainscoted rooms. In the dining hall, whose ease and comfort contrast pleasantly with the newly built cafeteria at the center of town, the "upper two hundred" of Los Alamos lunch when they do not prefer to go home. At our table was a chemist who had just taken over the function of public prosecutor under a newly evolved system of increased political self-government. "I shan't have much to do," he said with a shade of regret, "we're all too good. With luck I'll be able to get after a traffic offender."

"Even so, we *are* regular guys up here," put in another neighbor. "If only the people outside would realize that we atomic physicists and chemists are quite as human as themselves. To judge by some of the letters I get we're considered magicians, or worse still—robots. Do say if you speak of Los Alamos that we don't wear magicians' hats, neither do we have electronic brains in our heads nor Geiger counters in our bosoms. We're not monsters. No, sir!"

To prove to themselves and the world that they live, after all, as in any other American city, the residents of the Hill have started a great many clubs. In addition to the local branches of nation-wide lodges and brotherhoods such as the Lions, the Elks, the Kiwanis, the Optimists, there are societies for stamp collectors, pinochle players and skiers (for in the winter there are excellent slopes in the neighboring Jemez Mountains). The Model Train Association, the Duplicate Bridge Club, the Amateur Radio Club offer themselves to the new arrival side by side with such professional unions as the American Chemical Society or the Security Club.

A person to whom none of the eighty societies appeals, need still not spend his evenings alone. On every possible and impossible occasion people meet at parties. The fact that Los Alamos is semidry and that only clubs or private persons may serve drink is not solely responsible for the hectic social whirl. No doubt the factor that contributes most strongly to this brisk activity is the curiously isolated and supervised mode of existence. Where there are only Los Alamites there will be nobody to ask indiscreet questions. And should someone under the influence of alcohol talk on subjects better avoided, there is no great harm done in a circle of initiates. Besides, it rarely goes very far. If a man begins to grow talkative, somebody will certainly step in and admonish him with a gesture—now become a convention—of turning a key: "Shut up!" Whereupon the talker generally does shut up.

But at four in the afternoon when Mr. S., after the third or fourth drink in the empty Army and Navy Club, suddenly lost his self-control, only the dozing barman and I, his guest, were present. He had by now shown me, with praises, just about everything on the Hill that may be shown. I had successively seen the Supermarket with its antiseptic counters, the Community Center with a large motion-picture and lecture room, the editorial office of the Los Alamos *Skyliner,* the public library, the wireless station and the hospital.

Mr. S.'s unending song of praise had turned upon babies, dogs, skiing slopes and other pleasantly irrelevant details. Los Alamos, birthplace of the atomic bomb and its still more violent progeny, must on this showing have been a sort of watering place. But suddenly the beautiful picture seemed to look a bit silly to the good man himself. He interrupted the flow of his language with a loud: "Oh nuts. . . . To tell the truth, sometimes you'd like to smash a windowpane."

The barman looked up and immediately nodded again when no order came. Mr. S. screwed up his face, remembered that he was not with one of his fellow prisoners in the big house of glass, and turned silent. The window was tightly shut again and let only rosy pictures through.

Naturally he was sorry to have let himself go. As if to efface the impression he invited me to his home. Without talking we drove over to the "Western Area" where, on artificially watered lawns, arranged like clean little green bed rugs in front of small stand-ardized houses painted in bright Easter-egg colors, children were playing baseball. A rather paunchy man with thick eyeglasses was zealously pushing his electric lawn mower, and looked up at us with a friendly greeting. "That's George Gamow," said Mr. S. "You may have heard of his book on *The Birth and Death of the Sun*. One of our most important people here. His specialty is the hydrogen atom."

The afternoon was glorious. Mr. S.'s wife, who had the license for the only travel bureau of Los Alamos, talked with animation about the affairs of the day. "You'd never guess how many travel-mad people there are up here," she said. "Some of them spend half their salaries on week-end trips to New York and Chicago. Isn't it crazy?"

"It's all the better for you," observed Mr. S.

In the evening Mr. S. wanted to give a little time to his family. He had to help his daughter with some geography homework. But since my bus did not leave until late, he offered me the choice of a discreetly supervised visit to a movie or a call on an Austrian family who would be pleased to see someone from the old country. Naturally I chose the latter. Mr. S. dropped me at about seven o'clock at a house in a bright little row and promised to pick me up again in two or three hours.

We heard wonderful long-playing records. Recordings of the Brandenburg concertos. Then the Vienna Philharmonic and Schubert's *Lieder*. For the moment my hosts and I forgot we had become acquainted more than five thousand miles away from Vienna, in the desert of New Mexico on a rock bewitched by the whole apparatus of modern technique and secrecy. The dinner, too, served in the charmingly arranged living room, recalled the time of cultivated bourgeois pleasures now much farther than five thousand miles removed from us.

At last I tried reluctantly to lead the conversation back from the past and nostalgia to the present and workaday reality. My question to the gentleman of the house, a distinguished physicist, ran something like this: "How can you, who left your country because you desired a freer life, bear this existence with all its security rules and unavoidable restrictions of liberty?"

The brief, rather weary answer was: "One gets used to it."

"Yes, one gets used to it," repeated his wife with a distinct sigh of resignation.

Habit, the calming, but also the lulling power, split as atomic energy itself, is the key to so much at Los Alamos. "Aren't you afraid of blowing up one day along with your laboratories?" This is the standard question put sooner or later by every visitor from below. It is answered with an indulgent smile: "I was at first, but you soon get over that. If the fire department didn't occasionally organize a drill we'd never so much as think of that possibility. Habit . . . you know."

But the man from the world of rumors and conjectures presses indiscreetly on: "How do you manage to keep so many secrets? How can you bear never telling your wife a word about your work?" They laugh. "I know my Lohengrin," says the lady. Then, more seriously: "Even if Walter did tell me something, I'd be most unlikely to grasp it. And if I grasped it, I still shouldn't know very much about what's going on over there in the tech area. There isn't *the* atom secret, there are dozens, probably thousands, and I think no single man has a view of them all."

But the Atomic Energy Commission cannot rest on "security through ignorance." A warning poster hangs in nearly every Los Alamos office. It shows a man caught in radio waves like a spiderweb reading a report marked "classified." Underneath are the words: "Now that you know, control your wave lengths." The poster is an admission of the fact that all the walls, rails, barriers, all the interrogations and re-examinations are of no avail unless the "secret carrier" himself has the inner will to co-operate.

At the end of the war there were many scientists in Los Alamos who felt unable to continue their submission to its rule. That was the time of conscientious scruples when the leading workers on the first atomic-bomb development turned their backs on the Hill, meaning to devote themselves to freer, more peaceful forms of research. Not all, but a surprisingly large number, found their way back to Los Alamos in the years that followed. The Russian rejection of the United Nations' plan for atomic control justified the continuation of work on the atomic weapon in the minds of many American scientists.

Added to this was the realization that only the laboratories of Los Alamos had at their disposal certain instruments and facilities essential for advanced penetration into the secrets of matter. None of the many American universities is technically so well equipped as Los Alamos. The state is today the sole owner of certain means of production of scientific knowledge. A majority of atomic scientists are therefore faced with the alternatives of renouncing the continuation of fruitful work in their special field or of accepting the conditions laid down by Los Alamos and the other institutions depending on the Atomic Energy Commission.

"What holds me here more than anything else is the special microscope I work with," declared my Austrian host.

"Is it true that when you give up your contract with the Atomic Commission you mayn't go abroad for five years?"

"Yes, that's so. . . ."

"That's the thought that troubles us the most," said his wife.

"On principle, you understand. Because it strikes at one of the most important freedoms—freedom of movement."

"But believe me," the physicist broke in, "one . . ."

"I know, I know . . . one gets used to it."

Toward ten in the evening Mr. S. called to bring me safely to the bus which would make its last trip from the Main Square, in front of the Community Center, down to Santa Fe. I thanked him heartily for all his patience and sent cordial greetings to his wife before stepping with a light heart into the vehicle that was to carry me away from the bewitched world of the future.

As we parted we promised each other to meet again in Washington.

Unfortunately nothing came of that promise. Almost immediately after my visit to Los Alamos Mr. S., as I learned from the newspapers, vanished without notice. At first the press believed he had made off with atomic secrets and I feared that perhaps they might think he had given them to me. But when ten days later he was handed over to the American authorities in Mexico, the explanation turned out to be far less sinister. He had taken money with him which he had collected for charity, and either drunk it up or simply squandered it on all the experiences that he had sorely missed in Los Alamos. Naturally, Mr. S. was dismissed from that City of the Virtuous.

A BIT OF HELL

Richland, Washington

"DON'T PICK UP ANYTHING you see lying in the street or in the fields," the Richland parents, who are employed by the Hanford Plutonium Works, tell their children. "Absolutely nothing, do you understand?"

And to underline their prohibition they tell the story of the White Man.

"Once there was a watchman from Richland who found a tool while going his rounds and picked it up and brought it home although it didn't belong to him," the story opens. "It wasn't till the next morning that he noticed that his hands had become contaminated by alpha rays and he ran in fright to H.I. Division. Then the doctors and the watchman's superiors began to dither and to make a great uproar. They drove at once to the little house where he lived with his wife and children, to get back the tool as quickly as possible. But the contagion in it had already spread everywhere: not only the watchman and his family had to go to the hospital but also the whole house was sick. So the White Men with the black rubber masks had to be called. They ordered the beds, tables, chairs, pillows and in fact everything that could be moved to be taken away and burned. Then they had the paint scraped from the walls, the floors torn up and the kitchen stove dismantled. For everything, everything had been poisoned. . . . And if you're disobedient, the White Man will come to us too and take all the toys away with him, and the bedroom, the dining room, the kitchen and perhaps the whole house. . . ."

The story of the White Man is no cautionary tale invented for pedagogical purposes. It really happened in May, 1951. There are sheaves of documents relating to it in the archives of the Atomic Energy Commission and of General Electric which, under a mandate from the state, administers the atomic factories of the U.S.A. The incident itself could not be suppressed. Too many people in the neighborhood of the "poisoned house" knew about it. Only the watchman's name was kept secret. It was not wished that his children should be treated like pariahs at school, that the shops should refuse to deal with his wife because they did not want to receive money from her hand, that he himself should be avoided as one who has the plague. For his nearest neighbors had already done all that to him. Only when he moved from Richland to Kennewick, its sister town, where nobody knew of his mishap, was he able to live in peace again.

One cannot take the neighbors' alarm greatly amiss. In Richland, the brand-new, spotlessly clean town of thirty thousand inhabitants, built at the close of the war for the employees of the atomic factory twelve to twenty-five miles away, fear of contagion through the invisible radioactive particles and rays amounts to an obsession.

In public and continually repeated courses everyone who comes to live in Richland learns the atomic age's alphabet of fear:

Alpha rays. Positive charged helium nucleuses emanating out of the atom. Cannot penetrate the skin but can do great damage if they enter the body through small open places.

Beta rays. Electrons. Slight power of penetration. Penetrate about a third of an inch through the skin. Great danger of burns.

Gamma rays. Can penetrate from the outside deep into the body. Weaker in the mass than other forms of rays but the most difficult to ward off by protective measures because of their strong penetrative power.

Neutrons. Danger! Harmful in the highest degree. According to speed they penetrate different depths into the tissue. In the case of strong radiation internal organs are paralyzed.

The force of the threat is matched by the strength of the defense against it. Dr. Compton, head of the scientific armaments development in the Second World War, stated before the Special Committee of the Senate: "The atomic energy program involves by far the most dangerous production process ever undertaken by man." In 1942 some of the American atomic experts still believed it would be practically impossible to protect the workers in the atomic industry, then existing only on paper, against the rays produced by nuclear fission. Until then there had been altogether about three pounds of radium in human possession. Now in the nuclear burners literally millions of pounds of radioactive material of widely different varieties were generated by the influence of the atom demolisher. The scientists saw clearly that enormous quantities of life-menacing rays were being generated as by-products of nuclear fission. Safety measures of such scope and severity had to be taken as had never before been remotely necessary in the protection of industrial health.

The geographical location of the Hanford area, where the various divisions of the plutonium works are housed, fulfills the safety requirements. In the dry, barren inland desert of Washington State in the remote Northwest of the United States, an area of nearly six hundred square miles was enclosed. Pasco, Kennewick and Richland, which are gradually growing together into one town, lie eight to twelve miles from the entrance to the factory grounds, and twenty-five to forty miles from the windowless, gray cement, fortresslike block in which the actual process of the transformation of uranium ore into the artificial element plutonium (Pu 239) takes place.

For miles after entering the segregated area one sees nothing different from the other side of the barrier: dry ground overgrown with dusty sagebrush, a few frightened prairie dogs scurrying before automobiles, the railway to the factory guarded by soldiers of the Fifth Army and, finally, on the distant horizon, the metal chimneys, pencil thin, painted in the same dull camouflage colors as the first warehouses which now come into view. The constantly reappearing placards, a sinister variety of the loud advertising posters to be seen along normal American roads, are a reminder, as one approaches, of the particular nature of the spot. "SILENCE MEANS SAFETY," they warn.

But that is only the beginning. Inside the works the admonitions follow you step by step:

DANGER! STAY OUTSIDE. FLOOR HEAVILY CONTAMINATED

or

DANGER! RADIOACTIVE RAYS

or

DANGER! HIGH NEUTRONIC FLUX

The posters exhort:

PUT ON RUBBER SHOES! CONTAMINATION BEYOND THIS POINT

or

DO NOT FORGET GLOVES! HOT REGION

or

TIE ON MASK! AIR UNCLEAN

The posters direct:

CONTAMINATED GLASSWARE! SWITCH ON THE COUNTER BEFORE USE

or

DANGER OF RADIATION! SEE THAT GLASS IS FILLED WITH WATER

or

SHOULD ANYTHING BE SPILLED:
1. HOLD YOUR BREATH
2. LEAVE THE ROOM AND LOCK
3. IMMEDIATELY NOTIFY THE HEALTH DEPARTMENT

Next to the warnings is always the special symbol signifying danger: three purple radial segments arranged round a dark point.

These lists which hang in all the halls, passages, work and observation rooms of the Hanford Works are only a few voices in the unceasing chorus of warnings against the invisible poisoned rays.

There are the dosimeters which look like fountain pens and change color when the bearer has been too long exposed to radiation. Danger when green turns to yellow. High time to leave the workroom when yellow changes to orange. There are the brooches with a self-developing film which darkens, rings whose inset turns black, water taps which tell by their paint whether they are cool, warm, semihot or hot. Mechanical sniffers emit screaming sounds when the air becomes too strongly saturated with harmful particles. A man who enters the most dangerous regions is put into fantastic disguises and must feel his way with a long staff to whose tip a Geiger tube is fastened.

Countless are the measures against radioactivity. Sharp chemical soaps and fluids attack the remains of radiation on the clothes or hair. A chronic scrubbing, brushing and washing goes on. As in a bad dream one tries to scour away an invisible spot, a stain which one is never quite sure of having removed. For no one can as yet say with certainty whether the effects of the work with radiating elements may not appear years hence. Monthly as well as special half-yearly and yearly blood and secretion tests must be made by the Health Division on every employee of the Hanford Works. How many tiny particles may have entered the circulatory system, the liver, the gall, kidneys or spleen? Have the lymphatic glands suffered, is the spinal cord affected? How high is the number of white blood corpuscles? Are there deposits in the bone tissue? These examinations are obligatory and unceasing.

To work under such conditions a man must be fearless. But he may neither belong to the phlegmatic group, who often appear to advantage in dangerous situations through lack of temperament, nor may he take the considerable risks of his occupation too lightly. Here again, as with the jet pilots, a man of quiet, even temperament is sought, the intermediate type possessing neither too much nor too little initiative and imagination.

A man newly entering the army of nearly a thousand workers in the Hanford area is given, before ever he sets eyes on one of the factories, a four-weeks' course of instruction by lectures and educational films. Here he is taught that because of the dangers of radiation he will often work more fussily and slowly than he has been accustomed to doing. He learns that he will presumably never lay his own eyes upon the dangerous material with which he works, that he may approach the infected caps, screws and other machine parts, if at all, only with special tools a yard long. But above all, the new man will make the acquaintance of his guardian angel who will never leave his side for more than two or three hours during his working time in the plutonium factory. This is the H.I. man in white, employee of the Hanford Health Instrument Division, which is responsible for the protection of health in the factory. To every four persons occupied in the "hot regions" of the works there is at least one health guardian. He takes many tests a day to find out whether any of his protégés may have received more than the biologically assimilable dose of rays, and places a precise dossier before each individual entrusted to him, in which day by day, week by week, the current data relating to his health are entered. If, in the H.I. man's opinion, a worker who has done a particularly "hot job"—such as a repair or the removal of radioactive waste—has received too high a dose of dangerous rays, he can send him home on his own responsibility for the rest of the working shift or, under certain conditions, even for several days.

When the atomic worker, John P. Bryant, comes to the factory in the morning he is handed at the entrance two ionic chambers in pocket form, known as "pencils," and his personal brooch containing a small bit of film sensitive to rays. First of all he goes into the canteen to deposit his lunch, which he has brought along from Richland. There are no kitchens here because for reasons of safety no food may be cooked or served within the Hanford Area. Although the dining hall is far from the atomic ovens, in a "clean region," the tables are inspected at half-hourly intervals with Geiger counters for the possible presence of beta or gamma radiation, or with the portable alpha-radiation counter, known as "Poppy"; for the most feared and dangerous form of poisoning is the penetration of small particles into the stomach and intestines during the intake of food.

Now Mr. Bryant goes to the dressing room where he leaves his own clothes, and daily finds in his locker fresh underwear, socks, cleaned overalls, working shoes painted yellow on the tips and heels, a tight-fitting head covering, cellophane-wrapped gloves and protective goggles. Now he crosses the white line which divides the clean zone from the intermediate zone. Here, at the end of his working period, he will take off his strange uniform to step naked into the shower room watched by inspectors and equipped with special disinfectant soaps. At present the worker does not pause in the intermediate zone but proceeds directly to the hot region whose photoelectric door opens automatically before him.

Now he is standing in a high, bare, windowless room known as "the canyon," and waiting for his H.I. man who will make the first control tests of the morning upon him. No sooner is this accomplished than the foreman fetches him and brings him to his place of work. The colleague who has been on the night shift gives him a friendly glance through protective goggles. The men who relieve one another cannot even exchange a friendly slap on the shoulder. The predecessor shows the newcomer the log book of the atomic furnace in which the exact reading of the various measuring implements is recorded at regular intervals. Then John P. Bryant remains alone before a high wall without door or crevice but full of dial plates, pressure gauges, scales on whose finely marked graph paper curves are drawn in variously colored inks. Now for a few hours the worker will control the implements for control, supervise the instruments for supervision, will from time to time press buttons, turn wheels or move levers through which, behind the wall many yards thick, radioactive material is being mixed, receptacles emptied, uranium cartridges introduced and expelled.

There, behind the mighty shield, rages an inferno of radioactive rays. To encounter them for a matter of seconds would mean certain, even if creeping, death. Through a loud-speaker attached to a microphone connected inward, John P. Bryant can tell that something is really going on beyond the bare silent wall. Sometimes it sounds like the chirping of crickets in the summer meadows which now seem infinitely far away.

At ten twenty-one during the morning shift John P. Bryant is conscious of something amiss in his atomic oven. The instrumental slate pencil on his vibration gauge has crossed the red danger line, the loud-speaker is sending an entirely new melody out of the interior of the burner. It is as though the cricket had associated himself with another animal, as though his little metal tongue were whetting itself angrily against metal teeth.

Bryant immediately notifies the overseer, who after brief inspection applies to Technical Division 200. Canyon 7 of Group S begins to fill with people. Engineers have hastened to the spot. A number of H.I. men are standing in readiness. Bryant's white guardian angel wishes to take radiation measurements on him at once and leads him quickly away. Meanwhile the organization's chain reaction is set going. Word is passed to the emergency Station at Richland which, in case of an improbable but not impossible explosion, would take charge of the rescue work. Twelve minutes later the signal to stop work resounds through the cement gorges of the canyon. The plant, which operates uninterruptedly day and night, weekdays, Sundays and holidays, must be closed for repairs.

Occasional repairs to the machinery are as inevitable in the Hanford Plutonium Works as in other factories, even though here in the construction of reservoirs, supply lines and mixing apparatus, care was taken to use particularly resistant material. A group of new resistant metals such as titanium, germanium and zirconium has been intensively developed in the United States with a particular view to their employment in atomic installations. For in the realm of radioactive danger the replacement of a malfunctioning part becomes an endlessly awkward, time-wasting and dangerous operation.

It is totally impossible for a human being, however strong his protective clothing, to enter the atomic furnace. The defective part must therefore be unscrewed by a remotely controlled grasping implement and then brought to a sealed region especially prepared for these occasions.

The preparation of this repair place, which must lie as close as possible to the site of the damage, is the first task of a small special group. It erects provisional walls of leaden tiles, provides for the installation of strong light fittings and spreads a layer of removable artificial material over the floor which will thereby be protected from contamination. It is on this spot that the remotely controlled grasping tool will lay the faulty piece.

This grasping implement, doomed to remain forever behind the thick walls of the furnaces because of its hopeless radioactivity, is a sort of robot whom the plutonium workers have named "Sweet Hot Dolly." She does not look in the least as the layman tends to picture a robot. Robots—and there are thousands of these mechanical slaves in the U.S.A. today, equipped with subhuman intelligence but often superhuman sense and memory organs— seldom appear in forms resembling the human body. Their creators do not care to make them in their own image; at most they bear a likeness to an organ overdeveloped to serve a purpose. Thus there are robots who are all eye, others who are all ear; that is, their seeing or hearing capacity, untrammeled by considerations of proportion to other organs, is superdimensional. Dolly, for instance, is all hand and arm. She requires only a small brain which needs to obey the fairly simple directions of the wireless controller, but on the other hand, her ability to touch, feel, hold and carry things is above the average. Earlier types of Dolly could make only straightforward motions, the new types can copy and combine all seven fundamental movements of the human hand.

The master of Sweet Hot Dolly, sitting in his cabin protected from radioactivity, begins to direct his creature into the interior of the atomic furnace. As he touches the button of the televisor and the picture flares up, he can see the robot's massive white painted body in the jungle of pipes, boilers, valves and levers

behind the thick wall of lead and cement. Now he begins to move
the lever, which has been placed on his left, and immediately
this movement transmits itself across a distance of over a hundred yards to Dolly's left arm. She gropes in the gray metal laby-
rinth, she hesitates at a certain point. Her twitching movement
conveys itself back to the lever in her master's hermetically closed
berth. Without a doubt her sensitive electronic "feeling system"
has discovered an irregularity, a fractured place in the organs of
the oven. The master switches on a second television screen, puts
on a pair of special glasses and now obtains by the combination of
the two televisors a single three-dimensional, solid-looking picture on which a fresh white break in a transmission box is plainly
recognizable.

Now the robot hand begins to work. It flexes its joints, it takes
hold of the machine part with its unbelievably dexterous fingers,
loosens it, detaches it, is holding it. Dolly is guided through the
long walk in the interior of the furnace to a precise spot. For a
split second the heavy protective wall soundlessly opens a crack,
lets out the object brought by Dolly and falls shut again. The defective part is now lying on the repair place in the sealed region.

The repair crew is standing ready. They are four mechanics, a
foreman and naturally an H.I. man. They were chosen not only
for their abilities but above all on account of their health records.
Only workers whose total dose of radiation since they came to
Hanford is reasonably slight can be appointed for such a job, in
which overradiation is unavoidable even if only for a brief period.

Two members of the repair crew remain at the entrance to the
sealed region. They are the reserves. Wearing double white overalls, two pairs of gloves, high rubber boots, tight-fitting head
coverings and masks to which oxygen is being conveyed from
their own reservoirs, the four men now stand before the defective, highly radioactive part.

In the view of the great danger inherent in the repair work, it
would be simpler to do away with the whole damaged part and
replace it by a new one. This does not happen because a "bit of

hell," once it is outside the oven, is not so easy to get rid of. Its transport to the radioactive refuse pit would involve far greater difficulties than its repair. If a damaged part can really not be mended, it must be quickly walled in on the spot. All over the hot zone of the Hanford Works one sees here and there in a room, without any regular arrangement, little molehills of leaden tiles, like prehistoric tombs. The all-too-living atom particles and rays are beating against the walls; it will be thousands of years before they lose their fatal power.

In the case of the transmission box of atomic oven 7, the operation proceeds normally. With instruments mounted on long pliers, the two fitters succeed in mending the breach. But, stop! When the work is nearly completed and probably not more than two or three minutes would be needed to finish the job, the H.I. man gives two of the three masked figures a nod meaning: stop at once. Almost reluctantly the two workers leave the sealed region. Something in them refuses to believe in what is unseeable and unfeelable. But they are sufficiently experienced to know that their H.I. guardian angel has sent them away in their own interest, that just the additional fraction of a second needed to bring the job to completion might suffice to cause great damage to their health. The two reserve men move in immediately and finish the work of their predecessors.

A whistle announces the successful termination of the operation. Only when everyone has moved to safety will Sweet Hot Dolly reach out from within the furnace for the mended part and fetch it back into the atomic purgatory. The sirens sound: Section S, one of the six great units of the Hanford establishment, begins to work again.

Not far from Richland I was shown a quietly grazing flock of sheep. These, it seems, are plutonium tasters. As long as they keep well people need have no fear. For just as distrustful despots used to have their nourishment tasted first by a slave for fear of poisoning, so the health guardians of atomic factories send experimental animals on ahead to test whether the filtered but still, under certain atmospheric conditions, dangerous waste gases may not continue doing biological harm.

On the day when I saw the animals they were bustling about happily. The A.E.C. could write in its logbook: "The quantity of radiation in the atmosphere surrounding the Hanford area is slighter today than in the city of Denver, exposed to space radiation by its greater height above sea level."

The safety system stretches well beyond the immediate vicinity of the factory grounds. Mobile control stations with radiological testers take daily measurements within a circumference of one hundred and twenty miles. They concern themselves particularly with the danger of contamination which threatens the mighty Columbia River, part of whose water is used for the cooling of the atomic ovens. Not only is this water detained in special basins and chemically treated until it is only feebly radioactive, but the seaweed, driftwood and fishes, in which radioactivity may have gathered, are also systematically examined.

Most strongly supervised of all are the "burial grounds" in which radioactive refuse is interred. These are dismal squares in the desert surrounded by red painted cement stakes. Each is under the care of a "burial operator," an atomic cemetery custodian, and is serviced by heavily masked workers.

Here, in long deep graves are buried the contaminated objects made of solid materials, such as receptacles, cans, metal caps, under a layer of earth a yard thick. Fluid refuse goes from the factory through subterranean pipes directly into deep underground tanks. These atomic graves increase in dimensions year by year. They provide the Atomic Energy Commission with more headaches than any other phase of its activity.

For the materials buried here in the northwest inland desert will outlive us, the generation who have freed them through nuclear fission, by thousands, in part even by millions, of years before they lose their life-destroying power. Therefore the graveyards must be marked so clearly and durably that each succeeding generation will know to shun them. Woe if the knowledge of the exact position of these poisoned zones were to be lost in the course of time!

But there is also the danger that the "buried" in the Hanford graveyard may not be lying as quiet as their custodians wish. It is possible, even probable, that the radioactive poisons may be gradually working their way through the subsoil water and conceivably even through the layers of earth to regions not yet contaminated. A constant supervision of the entire geological substructure not only during our lifetime but increasingly during the lives of our grandchildren, great-grandchildren and more remote descendants is therefore indispensable. All other attempts at "removal of waste" through encasement in cement blocks which were sunk into the sea, interspersion with certain forms of bacteria and seaweed, mixture with special sorts of loam, have so far shown themselves uncertain and not particularly promising. There has even been some thought of the possibility later on of shooting the bits of refuse with rockets out of our atmosphere into space. Only in this way, it is said, shall we be truly rid of them.

"In the long run," a research worker at one of the Hanford laboratories said to me, "this problem seems weightier to me than the question of atomic-weapon control. For even if the powers were finally to agree and an atomic war should never be fought, the fact still remains that by splitting the atom we have released life-destroying forces into the world with which the future will have to deal. With each century it will be more difficult to control the mounting quantity of atomic waste. Everything made by man has faded, fallen into ruin or rotted within measurable time. For the first time we have produced something by our own interference with nature which if not eternal, is, by our measures, nearly eternal. A dangerous inheritance which may far outlive all our other creations, a bit of near-eternity: a bit of hell."

GOMORRAH IN THE DESERT

Las Vegas, Nevada

"Then the Lord rained upon Sodom and upon Gomorrah brimstone and fire from the Lord out of heaven." *Genesis,* xix, 24.

MRS. HELEN CHANDLER stood forlornly in the empty suburban street before her indefinably gray-green prefab, 294 Basic Road, and whistled again and again the first notes of the refrain of "Yankee Doodle." How long she had been whistling there before she stopped us I do not know. But her face was tired and tear-stained as she asked whether we had seen Duke. He was a small black dog of no particular race, with big ears, and he had run away from home for the first time. "When the bomb went off early this morning he wanted to crawl into my husband's bed. But John was cross at having been awakened by the noise and chased the dog out. Since then he hasn't come back. He was so frightened and his whole body was trembling." She handed us a slip of paper with her name and address. "His paws are white and also the tip of his tail," she called after us. And began whistling again.

Out in the desert near Frenchman's Flat the A.E.C. was experimenting with a new type of bomb.

Seven hours earlier Las Vegas had heard the ominous growl of the atomic explosion from a distance of a hundred miles. In Fremont Street the windowpane of Rex Bell's Western Supply Headquarters had been blown in. The glass was still lying scattered in countless large and small splinters over the display of broad Stetson hats, checked cowboy shirts and wide leather belts with convenient revolver holsters. Bell, a cowboy star returned from Hollywood to Las Vegas, is enough of a showman to seize upon the advertising value of such an occurrence. On the few panes of glass still hanging in their frames he had painted: "It's atomic." A superfluous bit of information. Everyone who walked or drove past Fremont Building stopped, in any case, to look at what the bomb had done.

Otherwise Las Vegas was entirely normal on this Saturday afternoon. That is, so far as a city which has made its money in a rapid succession of wild booms can be normal. In the year 1905 there was nothing here but a few tents and wooden barracks. Today Las Vegas calls itself (obviously it was an imaginative Chamber of Commerce that conferred this name upon it) "the magical city of the West." The slogan has a certain justification if one identifies magic with "black magic." For the town, which today has nearly thirty thousand inhabitants, draws several million tourists a year and proudly claims to have "three times as many neon lights per head of population as any other city in the U.S.A.," was built and grew on illusions.

The first illusion was the gold rush twenty-five or thirty miles to the east of the city. There two mineral prospectors called Bill Marsh and Harry Stimler had discovered a mine in December, 1902. So violent was the rush to the new gold fields that the Union Pacific three years later ran a railway line here. The new station was not in the actual mining town, Goldfield, but in Las Vegas. Goldfield, with its fifty-two blocks of houses, its hotel famous throughout the West for its large stock of French champagnes and the long bar with eighty barmen, is today a picturesque ghost town. The gold fields did not contain what they had promised. But Las Vegas, which had come into being because of the railway station and did well for itself as intermediary for the gold miners' food and equipment, outlived the disappearance of the *fata morgana*.

The other illusions to which Las Vegas owes its rise are homemade. First, of course, comes the gambling industry, which yields millions yearly. Should the city, as is being contemplated, embellish its square with a statue, it ought not to be dedicated to the founder, Archibald Stewart, but to the virtuous Senator Kenneth Johnson. This gallant man, who maintained a small illegal casino, was subject to pricks of conscience and accordingly devised a law to legalize all types of games of chance in the State of Nevada. It was accepted in 1931 by the state, which had been suffering from poverty of revenue. Thereupon, Nevada, as the only one of the forty-eight states in the Union to permit all forms of games of chance, became the Mecca of gamblers and of those aspiring to become gamblers.

Alternatively, the group of State Fathers, headed by Governor Fred Balzar, who had the courage to legalize quick marriage and divorce, should also come under consideration as candidates for the statue. Originally the interval before a divorce for people residing outside the state was six months. But when states like Florida, Arkansas, Arizona and Idaho reduced the term to three months, Nevada accommodated herself to our fast-moving times and magnanimously turned six months into six weeks.

The illusion that with the "yes" in a quick ceremony— "no witnesses, no formalities, no waiting"—the right to nuptial bliss could be purchased, drew and draws annually over twenty thousand couples to Las Vegas, who might have had second thoughts had they been obliged to comply with the health tests and waiting period prescribed in their own states. About seven thousand couples annually make use of the possibilities of painless divorce in Las Vegas and buy their illusory freedom from one of the sixty-one lawyers for sums of two hundred to twenty thousand dollars.

All these edifying facts I learned at the Chamber of Commerce. But the eloquent gentleman who delivered them was definitely nervous and worried. His smile went on and off like an illuminated advertisement in the "Glitter Gulch" that passes the gambling houses. The poor man has troubles. "This whole atom business is going to hurt us," he remarked in confidence. "It scares people. Who wants to be scared to death just when he's won a couple of thousand dollars? First of all, the women will stay away. They're the best clients for the automatic gambling machines. And if they don't come, that lets out the family business. That's sure. Most of our casino customers are married couples. The wife comes along because she's afraid the husband would overplay if he came by himself." On the other hand, my conversational friend weighed whether the trials at the newly installed testing ground might not be a good advertisement. "And free, at that," he consoled himself. He toyed with the idea of completing the little museum supported by the Chamber of Commerce, in which excavated arrowheads of the Stone Age are shown, by an exhibition of "Weapons from Prehistoric Times to the Atomic Era." If it should prove that the Atomic Energy Commission's promises were true about the safety of the tests for Las Vegas, then presumably the curious would come from all over the world. "And yet," he asked himself and me in a fresh access of doubt, "would they like to be disturbed on their honeymoon at un unearthly hour by an atomic explosion? It is not romantic. No, sir."

"I'll bet you ten to one that the bomb tests bring a thousand new visitors to Las Vegas," said the manager of the Golden Nugget, the biggest casino in town; "it's a bigger thing for us than the Hoover Dam. That brought thousands of tourists to Las Vegas who risked a few dollars with us on their way. But now the Hoover Dam is no longer the biggest. Grand Coulee up in Washington State is bigger and takes more sight-seers away from us every year. But the testing ground out there—boy, oh boy, Las Vegas will keep the monopoly on that. A winner."

It was now a trifle after three in the morning, but in the Golden Nugget as well as in its rival, Pioneers' Club, all the rooms were crowded with people passing the time at games of chance as they waited for the beginning of the atom test at half-past five. In the big hall at the entrance were rows and rows of gambling machines which clicked with a loud metallic tone when the money fell into the machine; the lever was released, and sometimes a pile of nickels or silver dollars tumbled out. Here and at the roulette tables they were "working" very hard by the light of daylight lamps. At

the dark mahogany-stained bar with its naked gilded nymphs, its
lustrous brass and copper, they were resting. In the reflection of
the mirror were seated guests who drank, dreamed and talked to
themselves.

Snatches of conversation which I was able to catch betrayed no
concern with the A-bomb. They were the old gambling mono-
logues, the same speculations about "nearly" and "if" and "almost" that one hears in Monte Carlo, Baden-Baden or Campione,
the eternal "if I'd only waited a little longer," or "red eleven
times running, *no* system reckons on that," or "if I'd only played
the pairs consecutively . . ."

"Yesterday you could see who were the real gamblers," the barman said; "the amateurs ran into the street when they heard the
bang but the professionals didn't even look round. When one of
the croupiers hesitated for a moment, they shouted at him, 'Go on,
go on . . . we aren't here for the fireworks.' "

It was toward four in the morning when the great motor parade
along Highway 95 began. Car upon car was driven from Las
Vegas up to Indian Springs, where the entrance to the testing
ground is located. It resembled the scene before one of the big
football matches on a Saturday afternoon—except that it was now
pitch dark. The automobiles turned on their great headlights. The
rocks along the road, washed by thousands of years of wind, sand
and river long dried up, resembled gigantic beasts: here a lizard,
there a camel, a dinosaur, an elephant's skull. The row of cars
came to a stop. Hooters and brakes, then silence. One could go no
farther and had to park at the side of the road.

It was very cold out there. Sharp, cutting desert air. As our eyes
became accustomed to the darkness we began to distinguish the
mountain ridges about twenty miles away: Spotted Range, Sheep
Mountains and Skull Range. Over them, explained those who had
watched yesterday's trial from a distance, the atomic sun would
soon come up. Along the other side of the road drove a white-
painted jeep. A loud-speaker mounted on it proclaimed: "Buy
protective glasses, the manual on atomic emergencies recommends

colored glasses. It is dangerous to look into the light without protection. Dangerous, dangerous . . ."

At five-forty it was beginning to be lighter. We could faintly see the barren ground, which looked unreal. The moonflowers, the ocotillo, the Spanish bayonet, the sand lilies, all the desert plants which seem to be asleep even in daylight. And then, as someone near us said: "Today there's nothing doing," the thing we had been waiting for happened. Silently out of the sapphire blue of the morning sky broke an immense glowing white flame. It seemed as though it were melting down the earth and all consciousness.

Involuntarily I had closed my eyes. When I opened them it seemed at first as though snow had fallen over the whole landscape, as though the mountains and craters and road were covered with a white cloth. Immediately afterward a wild mysteriously beautiful orange red seethed up, exotic and improbable as the interior of the calyx of a flower. And now appeared, slowly rising at the point where we had first seen the monstrous flash, a bluish violet circle of light. It was followed by the orange which had formed itself into a ball with black, red and dark gray fringes round its rim. The whitish violet supernatural light and the flame-colored orb flowed into one another, became a long-drawn-out cloudy white mushroom.

All this happened in utter silence. Later—a minute and a half after the rise of the great artificial sun—the dark sound of the explosion leaped at us. Instinctively we bent down. And now, warm, violent as the desert wind, came the impact. We straightened ourselves. Then it came again, this time at a shorter interval. First the rumble, then the hot breath of the explosion.

On the return journey nobody spoke. The horns did not honk. We crept back as in a funeral procession. The cloud of the explosion was now gray and dirty above us. A gigantic W slowly falling to pieces, through whose up-and-down strokes a sparkling silver control plane flew. On its wings lay the reflection of the sun. This time the real sun.

PART FOUR

Grasping at Nature

EARTHLY PARADISE

El Centro, California

I FIRST HEARD of Imperial Valley in one of those cheery truck-line cafés to be met with nearly anywhere between two widely separated towns at the most solitary points along the Western highways. These are places where the drivers of the gigantic express trucks climb down from their high seats behind the steering wheel after hours of travel for a gulp of hot coffee, a steak sandwich and above all a chat with colleagues coming from the opposite direction.

I have seldom seen these "highway jockeys" in agreement about anything. Friendly strife is their element. Their nerves are constantly strained. In the loud rumble of the motors they are often unable to speak a word for hours and must even swallow their curses at clumsy drivers. This is pleasing to their employers.

All the dammed-up communication and irritation can pour itself out when they stop for a quarter or half an hour at Rosie's Café, the Truck Driver's Home or Steak Heaven. It is all the more astonishing when these quarrelsome men for once agree. This was the case when the talk turned upon Imperial Valley. One of the drivers told how he had recently been paid a special premium for a shipment of tomatoes he had brought in record time from the valley to San Francisco, and from all sides other stories were immediately forthcoming about this strip of land, to which adjectives such as "fantastic" and "incredible" were applied.

This song of praise left a comparison in my ear. One of the

129

drivers had spoken of a man-made paradise. And I promised myself a visit to this earthly Garden of Eden.

I heard again of the legendary California valley when a colleague in New York served me with fresh strawberries in the middle of February. "They're not deep-frozen," he explained, "they've come by air from my wife's brother in El Centro. Just as we in Manhattan sell our morning paper the night before, so the harvests in Imperial Valley are predated. In December my brother-in-law harvests his spring vegetables and in the late spring he sends us mainly autumn grapes."

Generally such legends deflate more and more, the nearer one comes to their place of origin. But with Imperial Valley it was different. In Los Angeles, less than a day's distance from this region at the southern tip of California, the tales of wonder were more luxuriant than they had been farther east. "Down there you'll find the California they imagine in other countries," an orange farmer told me. "That's the most fertile bit of land in the whole world. Do you know, I've seen grapes from the valley as big as—practically as big as tangerines!"

When I finally asked at the Greyhound station on Sixth Street, Los Angeles, for a bus ticket to Brawley in Imperial Valley, someone behind me said: "Careful, son, that's the place where the farmers have to jump aside as soon as they plant a seed. Otherwise the thing comes up and hits them on the leg."

Like many a wonderland that stirs a people's imagination, Imperial Valley lies deep in the heart of a desert; it is, in fact, former desert transformed through a sublime human effort into an isle of plenty. I traveled from Los Angeles to El Centro at the end of December. Even at this time of year summer began as soon as we entered the desert. In Palm Springs, the resort of the Hollywood film colony, founded and made famous by clever real-estate agents, the Christmas guests were sitting in shorts and white frocks along the palm-fringed boulevard, and around the blue-green swimming pool people were acquiring their holiday tan. Only four months later it would be unbearably hot in the daytime, endurable only in air-conditioned houses. At a little wayside station in the midst of the rocky wasteland, I saw lizardlike reptiles sunning themselves at noon. Dry heat radiated back from dusty crags at the side of the road. But ahead of us in the middle of the highway rolled a couple of dewy fresh lettuces, dropped from a truck on the way from Imperial Valley. The great oasis could not be far off.

A hundred years ago this stretch of land was a terror to all who wished to cross it. It stood in the way of emigrants, like the Sahara. "When we traveled through this desolate region full of dry hot sand it was sown with discarded remains the emigrants had left behind, like the road of a retreating army," wrote Dr. Oliver Wozencroft in a travel diary published in 1849. "We found along our path dead or dying animals, guns, pistols, supply packets and other things that had made up the luggage of the unfortunates."

But in addition to such impressions of hopeless despair the doctor brought samples of earth out of the wilderness whose analysis convinced him that this arid land could be made fertile through irrigation. Remains of oysters and mussel shells showed that this basin, lying below sea level, had been covered in antiquity by the waters of the Pacific Ocean. The mighty Colorado River, flowing through the valley, had gradually dragged down on its back from the mountains so much earth and slime that it had heaped up a dam at its mouth and condemned the barred-off arm of the sea to slow desiccation.

It took fifty years for the California doctor's idea to be put into practice. At the beginning of our century the Colorado desert was still as desolate and frightful as when Wozencroft had described it.

But in June of 1900 the first canals were dug according to the plans of the Australian engineer Rockwood. Four years later the river rebelled, stepped out of its bed and used the new canals as gates for an invasion. From 1904 to 1907 the stream, in constantly renewed attacks, repeated the attempt to reconquer its valley. Stronger and higher dams were built, more fit to withstand the flood catastrophes. Finally, in the years 1928 to 1936, the powerful Hoover Dam high in the mountains, which with its gigantic cement walls placed itself daringly in the way of the Colorado, stopped it, and by its turbines guided it and was enabled to switch it on at will by means of locks.

Since then Imperial Valley has not needed to fear inundation. An extended system of canals, tributaries and enclosed brooklets has been dug to convey the river water into the former desert. Controllers at switchboards regulate the ups and downs of the locks, the water level in the trenches and side trenches. They can send the desired quantity of water into each "irrigation rectangle" of the four thousand, five hundred square miles. "At home we must pray for rain," say the Mexican casual laborers who work in the valley; "here they have only to phone 'central' and the water streams in!"

Imperial Valley makes a startling impression from the air. The view from the plane of that vast green garden set in the pale brightness of the sand dunes and interlaced with broad and narrow strips of water is a thing of splendor: a vision of abundance wrested from nature. The only elevations on these flat acres are high, geometrically arranged rectangular heaps of carrots, pyramids of onions, motley hillocks of grapefruit, cucumbers and avocados.

I was unprepared for being invited on a little flight, as naturally as elsewhere one is invited for a drive. But the big farmers and members of co-operative societies are flying enthusiasts. They have their fields sprayed from the air with chemicals against pests and diseases, send part of their crops by air freight in the winter months to the markets in the big American cities, and not infrequently fit up landing places on their own properties. There are landowners who fly from sixty to a hundred and twenty miles every morning to their farms in the hot valley or to the provision exchanges in El Centro, and back early in the afternoon to their homes on the Pacific, to Hollywood or to the mountains above San Bernardino.

More numerous are the owners who have practically ceased to concern themselves with their tracts of land and go for weeks or

months without seeing them. They have handed over the management of their properties to a co-operative which, with its machine
equipment, scientifically schooled agricultural engineers, their
packing house and own sales organization, can farm more dollars
out of the earth than would be possible for the single owner.

So the farmer becomes a sort of shareholder who has his dividends paid to him yearly by the co-operative, lives in town and in
some cases practices a different calling there. He is a salesman of
agricultural machinery, a vegetable broker, a real-estate specula-
tor. Sometimes he opens a furnishing business or supermarket in
the immediate vicinity of his fields, where his manager and
workers buy their provisions.

This does not seem too unlike paradise until one gets a closer
view. Only the minority of the absentee owners have left their
estates voluntarily. The others have been forced to it by the increasing mechanization and bureaucratization of agriculture. They
would not have had a chance in a lone fight against this development forced upon the valley by agricultural big business. A few
stubborn individualists who tried to hold out soon went bankrupt.
They could not compete with organized mass production.

The absence of frost and of weather fluctuations has made possible a systematic cultivation and exploitation of the soil modeled
on industry. In Los Angeles, Imperial Valley had been described
to me as a big natural hothouse. The more closely acquainted I
became with this extraordinary bit of land the more I had the
impression of having come upon an immense factory under the
open sky. Here the man-devised laws of rationalization and
intensification take precedence over the old laws of nature. Thus
the same fruits and vegetables could often be harvested three or
four times in the course of a single year. The work was organized
as on a large conveyer belt.

"From seed to dinner table in one month," asserted a "salad
manufacturer's" slogan I read in El Centro. I could well understand that if the situation on the produce market justified such an
effort, the limits set by darkness would be ignored. Several firms
have purchased searchlights from surplus army stocks and let their

people work the whole night through, to have their produce ready
before the season begins.

Of the seventy thousand residents now earning a living in the
wonderland where a generation ago only the beasts of the desert
dwelled, nine-tenths are workers and employees. The lowest stra-
tum is composed of seasonal laborers, legal or illegal immigrants
from near-by Mexico. They are employed where the new agricultural machines cannot as yet work more cheaply than manual
labor and are paid according to a fixed tariff. Socially a class
above the Mexicans are the American farm workers. They must
be skilled mechanics in the first place, and each year learn to
operate and service an increasing variety of machines. Many of
them know less about agriculture than a town worker who tends
a little garden on Saturdays and Sundays. But they do know in
detail the complicated mechanism of the onion-picking machine,
tomato shaker, hay binder and large family of tractors. "I hate the
smell of manure and love the smell of oil," one of these motor fans
said to me as he fitted a turnip-gathering appliance onto his
mechanical plow.

Technical agricultural knowledge is expected only of the
experts set above the casual laborers and field mechanics; these
are not themselves farmers, though occasionally they are farmers'
sons. They have graduated from agricultural colleges, and their
academic status places them on an approximate level with the
engineers employed in industry. They determine the course of
production on a scientific basis and are interested in increasing
the output of the soil and the efficiency of the worker. The stop-
watch, tape measure and motion study long successfully adopted
in factories are being introduced by these men into agriculture.

The packing houses have made particular strides in rationalization. Through the whole length of such a building run brooks
containing cleaning and coloring chemicals, into whose current carrots with earth stuck to them are poured from a mechanically tilted truck, to emerge at the other end clean and several
shades stronger in color. At once the binding machines seize them
and transport them in symmetrical bundles round a revolving

table, along a conveyer belt to the clippers which trim off superfluous green. Then they roll to the packers who throw a layer of
carrots and a layer of dry ice into passing crates. The last station is
a robot which nails the cases and shoves them into the waiting
truck. The lettuces take even less time, since they need not be
bundled. The tempo has been so speeded up that a single packing
house can now prepare as many lettuces for shipment as all
twenty were able to do in the days of handwork.

The only bottleneck in the ever broader and swifter stream of
production is slow and tedious Nature. To spur her to a faster pace
is the task of the valley's experimental station in Meloland near
Brawley. "One of our problems was the tomato crop," said the
young University of California research worker who received me.
"Tomatoes ripen irregularly. On the same cane you get a fruit
whose red skin is nearly bursting, another still green and a third
that has just begun to turn pink. So long as this continues to be the
case, the bushes must be hand plucked at a variety of times. Now
we have developed mechanical tomato pickers which will shorten
the harvesting process. But in order to make use of them, we had
first to produce a shrub whose fruits would ripen as nearly as possible at the same time. Besides, the tomatoes had to loosen themselves from the bushes earlier than they used to so that the machine would not have to shake the plant too hard. And the skin
had to be more resistant so as to remain undamaged by the fall
into the mechanical picker's basket. Now, with the help of other
institutes working on similar lines, we have evolved such a tomato.
If Nature doesn't co-operate with our new time-saving machines
we must and can compel her to."

The Meloland experimental station is a comparatively
small outpost of the "green revolution" being carried from the
laboratories into American agriculture. Behind it stand larger laboratories of natural biology in which, among other things,
the process of plant growth through radioactive tracing material is
being explored with unprecedented thoroughness, thousands of

crossbreedings are being attempted and entirely new species of plants produced by direct intervention in the genes of the seed.

These few white bungalows, these small experimental plots and humble-looking hotbeds in southwest California are mission houses of the conviction that the work of nature, down to the tiniest plant cell, may be observed, altered and improved upon. If in Meloland species of grass are invented which can resist great heat, if an unwithering flax is produced, a melon that will grow just big enough to fit the housewife's standard refrigerator and dates or almonds of the exact size required by the chocolate factories, these are practical local applications of an endeavor going much deeper into the life principles of Nature.

The "green revolution" in America no longer meets with opposition. The last generation of farmers mistrusted the ideas of the advocates of scientific methods. But the new generation, particularly the agrarian experts, the "fertility engineers," are differently disposed. "It used to take decades to get the farmers to change their methods," remarked the young research worker at Meloland. "Today they're as eager for our latest laboratory results as manufacturers for new inventions and patents."

That is particularly true in Imperial Valley, where the time-honored ways of land cultivation had never taken serious root. New methods are constantly tried for turning the paradise into a super-paradise. The great oasis grows farther and farther into the desert, the output is greater and greater. But there is a large *but*. A shadow hangs over the entire region, a thing they do not care to mention in El Centro, Holtville, Brawley and Indio. It is the ancient and all-too-living theme of a threatening flood, a deluge in the not-remote distance.

"A man-made paradise? I'd sooner call it a fool's paradise," said the queer old local editor who lives in a small town on the border of Imperial Valley; "but I can't write about it. People don't want to hear the truth. The landowners and estate agents bring pressure to bear because they're afraid the value of their property might go down. People try to ignore or belittle a serious danger that threatens thousands of people and millions in money. It's good to be able to talk about it for once."

It seems that man, in harnessing the Colorado, prepared the way for a more powerful enemy with more ancient rights in the great basin of Imperial Valley: the Pacific Ocean, which now, aided by the shortsightedness of the dam builders and irrigation technicians, threatens to return to its old bed.

In millenniums of labor the great river erected at its mouth in the Gulf of California a natural dike of considerable length and breadth in front of the basin which was later to become Imperial Valley. Each year the incoming tides of the ocean swallowed up a part of this dam, but the river, dragging daily about five hundred tons of sand, earth and slime on its journey through the Rocky Mountains and seven western states, would always repair the damage.

When in the thirties of the present century the river had the yoke of the great new dam laid upon it, it was forced to leave nearly all these natural building materials behind in the mountains. They now began to fill the artificial Lake Mead, behind the Hoover Dam. Thus they were absent from where they were most needed: several hundred miles to the south, to fight the greedy waves of the Pacific.

With astonishing speed the ocean availed itself of the situation arising from the disturbed balance of power. In 1940, only five years after the opening of the Hoover Dam, the tip of the Gulf of California had pressed forward fifteen miles into the land. Ten years later the whole former bank, an area of many square miles, was flooded by a lagoon, the Salada, daily increasing in size.

Far more dangerous than this slow influx of salt water is the attack of the tidal waves upon the foundations of the large alluvial land barrier. Twice a day, as I had occasion to see for myself, the surf tears great pieces of land from the shore and pulls them back into the depths of the gulf. Thus the height of the natural dike, which never exceeded thirty feet, has decreased in eighteen months by nearly half. The disappearance of the natural wall between Imperial Valley and the Pacific Ocean is a matter of time.

If this development is not arrested, the man-made paradise, its twenty-five settlements, its rich acres, its streets and open spaces, are bound to be overwhelmed by a flood of catastrophic proportions.

But strangely enough, the prospect of such an occurrence seems to trouble neither Congress nor the few informed inhabitants of Imperial Valley. Although serious authorities have issued warnings in articles appearing in the New York press, lame denials have been the only response. Probably the interest and pressure would be greater if the battlefront lay in American territory. The fact that the dike formed by the Colorado River, which protects America's most fertile soil, is on Mexican terrain in a region not easily accessible favors indifference to the threat of deluge. "If there is indeed a danger for Imperial Valley," say responsible voices in Washington, "it is the reverse of that. We consider a drought far more likely than a deluge." The root of this fear is to be sought in the structure of the Colorado Dam. It has been calculated that Lake Mead, behind the Hoover Dam, will eventually silt up with sediment from the river and a gradual stoppage of the water conduits become inevitable.

It was once believed that this would happen within a hundred years. More precise measurements have made possible a more optimistic outlook. Apparently it will take at least two hundred and seventy-five years for the blockage of the dam to become dangerous. Imperial Valley must count on a diminution of the water supply which made possible its rise from desert sand to garden oasis. "But who wants to think as far ahead as that?" asked a government official with whom I talked about the matter. "Let future generations find the answer."

"So you think 'After us the deluge'?" I inquired.

"Or the drought," he laughed. "But don't worry. By that time we'll find a solution. There are always new answers to new questions."

Thus he testified firmly to his belief in the duration of the earthly paradise.

THE WEATHERMAKERS

Denver, Colorado

THE OLIVE-GREEN Army aircraft ahead of us was swallowed by the cloud monster. We heard the thunder of its engines and immediately afterward saw it shoot out on the other side of the gigantic white beast. But there was still not a snowflake to be seen against the blue background of the sky.

From the second plane they signaled to us: "We'll have a try with the pistol." It was absurd to imagine a few shots with silver iodide cartridges having any effect on this quiet, vanishing, super-dimensional sky creature. "It must be at least two miles high and five miles long," my neighbor screamed into my ear. On the way up we had agreed to name our cloud Moby Dick after the gigantic, mythical whale.

Now the second machine had cut Moby Dick into two parts which strained toward each other with great speed and the next minute were reunited. The white cloud fish in the sea of heaven was jeering at us. His grimace was a challenge. The new attack had not succeeded, either, in forcing him to give up the moisture accumulated in his belly.

The pilot gave a signal. Now we were going at it. We were swimming a moment later in white fog. The plexiglass hood above us was covered with moisture. But there we were again out in the sunlight. "Snow," cried the man beside me who at some time while we were in the belly of the whale must have thrown out his receptacle with the bits of dry ice. It was a fact. The wings of our machine were covered with a light down, which at once transformed

139

itself into clear, glittering drops of water. We turned round and saw Moby beginning to dissolve in a dance of flakes which in falling melted into rain. Below us on the barren ground of the high plateau two men in light, wide straw hats stared up at the bursting cloud and then ran quickly out of its range, over to the edge of the great shadow, where the sun was shining with undiminished strength.

This happened at Albuquerque, New Mexico, when I was allowed to be present on one of the trial flights which are made regularly for the study of weather control. Since then I have become acquainted with a great variety of other "weathermakers." For example, the young people of the School of Mines at Socorro, New Mexico, who are proposing to control thunder and lightning. They hunt storm clouds with color-film cameras and radar instruments. When a particularly dark wall of cloud forms, they fly at it and bombard it with a variety of microscopic particles of metal whose nature they do not wish to state. "We're trying to alter the degree of electric tension before the burst. The object is to prevent lightning and provoke rain," the director of the school told me.

Then in Schenectady I saw in the laboratories of General Electric the simple apparatus with which young Vincent Schaefer "made weather" for the first time in July, 1946. In trials which took place on Mount Washington, Schaefer and his chief, Irving Langmuir, began to be interested in "supercooled clouds." These clouds, which moved in icy layers of air, contained moisture which, contrary to all logic, refused to freeze. It had been known for several years that snow does not fall from such clouds until the moisture crystallizes around a particle which has penetrated from the outside. This theory suggested to the German, Walter Findeisen, in 1938, that it would be possible to produce rainfall by the arbitrary introduction into the clouds of such tiny particles.

An ordinary icebox lined with black satin and having a particularly bright light inside it was used for the experiment. Schaefer first blew his breath into it, representing the "supercooled cloud," and next certain pulverized substances which were to be tried out as crystallization particles. One after another, he tried about a hundred materials. Among other things he sprayed graphite, quartz, sulphur, coal dust, various kinds of sand, finally even soap powder and talcum powder into the icebox. All in vain.

As so often with experiments, chance stepped in as a helpful ally. To lower the temperature of his box Schaefer one day threw in a handful of the dry ice lying about the laboratory and before he could confront his supercooled cloud with his newest preparation—genuine volcanic dust—suddenly the long-awaited snowflakes hung glistening against the black satin background. The crystallization particles had been found: tiny points of dry ice. They now caused a chain reaction in Schaefer's cloud of vapor. Each one of his snowflakes became two, two became four, four eight, until his whole black satin sky was hung with little frozen stars.

Almost at the same time, Schaefer's colleague, Bernard Vonnegut, was trying to find a snow-forming particle with which to shoot at snow clouds. In a manual dealing with the structure of nearly two thousand crystals he found one virtually identical with the dry ice crystal. This was silver iodide, hitherto used chiefly in connection with photography. After a preliminary failure owing to the insufficient purity of the silver iodide available on the open market, a second experiment with pure silver iodide particles produced excellent results.

Neither Schaefer nor Vonnegut hid their discoveries under a bushel, particularly after Schaefer, on November 13, 1946, successfully repeated his icebox experiment with a genuine cloud in the open air. As soon as it became known that one could "milk" the clouds by strewing dry ice or bits of silver iodide, dozens of sorcerers' apprentices appeared in the American skies. Particularly in the Southwest, always thirsty for rain, crowds of amateur weathermakers bobbed up. Some wished to call down rain from heaven simply for the fun of it, others began to do a flourishing business in rain magic. In this respect no one was so successful as Irving P. Krick, who made a million dollars in three years by sowing clouds with silver iodide.

Superficially the man with the soft, full face and the thick mane of gray hair, who has done big business in the pursuit of clouds, looks more than anything like the conductor of an orchestra. When the visitor remarks upon this, Krick snatches with pleasure at the idea. "In a way," he says, "my work has something in common with a conductor's. Only that my notes are the signs of the weather charts and my instruments silver iodide sprayers."

He goes to the big map of the fifteen western states and points at the little flags which take their position according to his weather instruments. "At one time or another we've placed fifty-nine sprayers at spots known to me as weather nooks," he says; "in addition to these, I have twelve movable ground generators mounted on trucks and five weather machines which can be operated from airplanes. They are thrown onto a weather front only occasionally, as a reinforcement at decisive moments."

Dr. Krick's firm, the Water Resources Development Corporation, is housed in a two-story building in Denver. Here weather reports come in day and night on teleprinters from all parts of the world. Twenty-eight meteorologists and an electric brain try to evaluate the incoming data in precise predictions. On the lower floor is the telephone exchange. It is permanently connected with the operators of the rain machines, distributed over a territory the size of all western and central Europe.

In Arizona, Colorado and New Mexico I saw these machines at work. They are insignificant little stoves forty inches high, of ordinary gray metal, reminding one at first glance of coffee grinders. Only that in the funnel, into which the beans would fall, little round charcoal balls are wandering about interspersed with silver iodide. The little balls arrive slowly, at regulated intervals of time, in a fire lit with gasoline. A fine stream of silver iodide scarcely visible to the naked eye is released in the flame and sent into the air by a sort of bellows. One would hardly believe this modest affair capable of causing heavy day-long snowfalls and downpours. The generators are said in some cases even to have deflected tornadoes.

Krick's earnings may be calculated from his tariffs. He is paid two to five cents an acre by the ranchers and farmers who make contracts with him. Should the rainfall on the property of the contracting party not rise above the average he need pay only a small lump sum, should it rain harder and more often his payments rise with every additional inch of water that falls from the sky. In 1951 Krick had under contract three hundred and thirty million acres, a territory as large as France. Nearly all his clients received more than average rainfall and paid Dr. Krick accordingly for the surplus. His receipts in that year alone were estimated at no less than ten million dollars, his outlay at under a million.

Of this outlay a considerable portion goes to insurance premiums for protection against possible claims for damages. A firm of molybdenum prospectors in the Rocky Mountains sued Krick for the cost of additional snow shoveling when he filled an order for a fifty-per-cent increase in the snowfall at the source of the Arkansas River. In other regions sporting clubs whose events were spoiled by rain, and holiday resorts whose hotels emptied when it poured at the wrong season, brought suits against Krick. He has been reproached with impairing the growth of pine forests with his silver iodide vapors, of conjuring up hailstorms and of causing traffic accidents by wetting the streets. All the irritation over bad weather—and the weather is always bad for somebody—has at last found a scapegoat.

But there are also enthusiastic Krick apostles. His warmest advocate has been the cattle breeder, Albert Mitchell, who grazes thousands of oxen and sheep on his New Mexican pastures. He called upon Krick in the summer of 1950 when a drought, already serious, threatened to become catastrophic. The weathermaker promised relief, and only a few days after he had installed his generators it was raining on Mitchell's property while most of the neighbors continued to suffer from the drought. Groups of them made pilgrimages to their competitor's green turf to see the marvel with their own eyes. "That was the most convincing proof of my claim," Krick told the visitor. "From then on we could hardly save ourselves from the deluge of bids for our services. And we furnished so much rain that by September the cattle grazers in New Mexico and Colorado were asking us to turn off the tap."

Dr. Krick has by now a great many imitators, some of whom, particularly his former collaborators, seem to understand their business; others who, through their exaggerations—they shoot their silver iodide particles into the atmosphere too frequently and in too large doses—fail in the first place to obtain the desired results and in the second have caused an incurable confusion in the weather household of the United States.

"The uncontrolled activity of weathermakers in the western states is bound to have consequences as yet unpredictable for the eastern ones," said Bernard Vonnegut, one of the inventors of weathermaking, in a hearing before a congressional committee. "It is a question of playing with powerful forces and ought not to be risked without competent supervision."

Dr. Krick is among those who believe that permits should be issued for weathermaking. "It is all the more important in that we shall be making greater and more decisive advances into the art of weather control," he told his guest. Then he began to speak of the possibilities in detail: from the capture of tornadoes to the utilization of the power potential of storms and tempests. The period he had granted the interviewer was over but he still found time for further explanations.

For he was waiting for his plane, which should have started long ago, but had repeatedly postponed its take-off. On account of bad weather of course.

THE ANIMAL AS A MACHINE

Des Moines, Iowa

THE FUTURE seems to belong to the "progressive" farmer in America, and to his methods of mass production. A man who prefers to farm in the old way has a hard time of it. I learned this from a well-to-do landowner whose acquaintance I had made the previous year when he was studying in Switzerland, and when I now telephoned as I passed through Santa Maria, his home town in California, I was told that he had gone into forestry, and caught up with him later in Sacramento.

"I've given up farming," he said as we sat over a glass of wine. "Naturally everyone thinks I'm a fool because prices for farm products have never been better than now. But I simply couldn't work with the modern methods. Or rather, I didn't want to. I went into farming because I like nature. Not to trespass on God's preserves and exploit his creatures as if I were a slaveowner."

His revolt had begun when the farmers in his neighborhood starved the bees. Professors in the agricultural department of the University of California had discovered that bees could be caused to do "more work for less honey." Their method was "very simple" as the agricultural papers expressed it. Six to ten times as many bees were made to swarm over a clover field as before. "The demand for nectar suddenly became larger than the supply," explained the specialists. The effect was telling. In their desperate search for nectar the bees did not leave a single blossom unopened, thus more plants were fertilized and the production of fodder greens rose five times per acre. Naturally the

145

hungry bees produced less honey and some, unable to adjust themselves to the new "struggle for existence" fell to the ground starved, but the beekeepers calculated that they earned more by "renting" their stock to the foodstuff producers than by the sale of honey. So all was well as far as they were concerned.

"The affair of the bees is only one sign of the radically changed attitude to livestock," said H. "Do you know that on progressive farms the baby pigs are removed from the sows so that the mother animals will pig three times a year instead of two? Their brood is reared on synthetic milk from an artificial udder, and to keep them from noticing the difference the grunting of a nursing sow is produced on a tape recording through a loud-speaker."

What H. meant by the new attitude I saw for myself when I was shown the model farm, about fifty miles outside Los Angeles, of Isaac Sharkarian, a "meat and milk manufacturer" of Armenian origin.

"We look upon our cows as machines," explained this successful farmer. "We put raw material in the form of nourishment into the machine and take out milk and butter. With our fast tempo of production the cows are generally 'burned out' after two and a half years. If we'd put them to graze for ten or twelve months they'd recover, but I have calculated that periodical disuse of the cows as milk machines is unprofitable. So I prefer to send them to the slaughterhouse and use the money buying young fresh cows."

Farmer Sharkarian's cows stood side by side in long rows before their feeding troughs which were automatically refilled. At shoulder height over each cow was a curious bow which the animals avoided timorously with every motion. "Electrically charged," explained the stable master who showed me round. "The animals know it, so they stay exactly in the place we've assigned to them. Like that it's much easier to keep them clean. They let their dung fall on the spot from which we can most easily remove it with the mechanical cleaning equipment. Don't you find these stalls nearly as clean as human living rooms?"

Indeed everything here was freshly scrubbed. Music sounded out of the loud-speakers and the electric milking implements hummed comfortably. The milk was pumped directly from the udder into a system of pipes in which it was cooled and then again pumped into the dairy's big tank wagons. "No milk pails, no dirt, no spilling and no turning sour," the foreman announced triumphantly; "it's the most hygienic operation in the world."

There are still herds in America roaming as formerly over large fenced-in pastures. I have seen them in the alpine meadows of Wyoming, the broad flat stretches of Texas and in the surroundings of Elko, Nevada, a typical cattle town with more heads of cattle than the entire population of the state. Here you will find cowboys wearing, as in the storybooks, broad-brimmed hats and high boots with silver spurs which have, however, more contact with the gas station than the flank of a horse. It is at least as important today for the cowboy to understand the moods of his Willys Overland as the breaking in of a horse. When he captures a runaway animal he uses the lasso as formerly but now it is woven out of nylon threads, and if a few head of cattle go astray on the broad range, often the size of a whole Swiss canton, a cowboy may well step into the one- or two-seater airplane which forms part of the equipment of many of the large-scale farms in order to find them again.

The cowboy of today has no guitar; instead he carries a portable radio. He no longer reads footprints and the rim of weather-predicting clouds but occupies his leisure with cheap comics issued in New York or Chicago, in which he may see his predecessors' long-vanished life of adventure gaudily illustrated. His traditional opponents, the cattle thieves, have also brought themselves up to date. They come at night with trucks, drug the animals they propose to steal and have special techniques for removing the owner's brand from the stolen animals' skin. The cowboy, perhaps the only surviving figure of Western folklore, is the symbol of the successful adaptation of the frontier tradition to the present era.

But more typical of our time is a man who practices a very different calling and plays a role of ever-increasing importance. On the cattle farms he is called simply "the engineer," or jokingly, "the big bull"; for his duty is to carry out the artificial insemination of cows.

Artificial insemination was first practiced on a large scale by the Soviet Union for speeding up propagation and improving the breed of cattle, pigs, sheep and horses. In 1936 Edward Sorensen introduced the Russian technique into Denmark, whence it was exported to the United States where the first successful experiments were made in 1937 in the Minnesota Agricultural School. Since then the movement in the United States has been expanding year by year. Hundreds of associations have been formed for the centralization of bull breeding and the distribution of the sperm of particularly valuable animals.

On receipt of a telephone call the engineer arrives at the farms belonging to the association. He brings with him the little phial of fresh bull semen in a thermos flask kept at a temperature of 40 degrees Fahrenheit. The sperm is heated over a flame to a temperature of about 115 degrees and injected with a glass syringe into cows in heat. With the impregnation engineer a new class of person has appeared on the cattle ranch. He is sober, educated, precise, a typical laboratory worker with university training and little time to spare for drinking or adventures. As soon as he arrives at a ranch he sets up a little laboratory in a corner of the stable, takes the temperatures of the cows in question, immunizes, sterilizes and makes notes on the "procreation statistics."

He carries with him the index cards on which are registered all previous successful and unsuccessful attempts at the impregnation of each cow concerned. His work proceeds with speed and precision. In the course of a day he normally "serves" two dozen cows at four or five different farms. The farm hands who lead the animals to him may laugh at his disinfectant, his rubber gloves, his needles and injections. He himself seldom alters his expression, silently snaps his little rectangular instrument case shut, takes the proprietor's receipt for each impregnation and drives to his next destination.

I asked one of these technicians, Jerry Polk, to take me, before starting on his daily rounds, into the breeding station which houses the syndicate's central bookkeeping office as well as the sperm givers. It was a gray day as we turned off onto a side road at about eight in the morning near Ames, Iowa, and drew up before a flat two-story house still smelling of mortar. An outdoor staircase brought us to a large office occupying the entire length and breadth of the first floor.

A secretary had prepared a list of today's "clients" and now shoved it onto the engineer's desk with a sullen gesture. Her sulky mood seemed to have overflowed onto the two other occupants of the room, one of whom appeared to be taken up with a large chart with dark green lines, the other with a small adding machine.

Had the view from the large window not given over the broad green cornfields of Iowa one might have imagined oneself in any town office. On the wall was a map of the region with the usual variegated little flags to which the secretary, after answering a telephone call, now added a new one. "Hereford K731 positive," she said.

"Well, at last," said Polk. "I'd given that up. Four times with no result. But Atomic D. Lamplighter the Third has brought it off again. A record animal."

He showed me into his small laboratory, separated only by a glass door from the rest of the office, and having at its center an icebox. "This is where we keep the semen," he explained, "and here"—he pointed to a row of glass vessels—"is where we thin it out. Nature is far too lavish with the precious stuff. In a normal procreation the bull wastes two hundred million spermatozoa; we have achieved excellent results with a hundredth part of that. We use white of egg to 'bulk out' the semen. Even in this solution it keeps its life for days if properly preserved. We had a particularly valuable bull here whose seed we had flown down to the Argentine; another of our animals has daughters in Holland and Denmark. Within the States we can send the sperm through the ordinary post if it's correctly packed. That gives us an interesting side line."

Actually I had no desire to watch the "service" of the bulls. A shyness which would scarcely have seemed comprehensible to the fertility engineer prevented me from asking him to show me this part of his work. But it was he who invited me to accompany him down to the stalls and be present at the "semen collection." In fact, he particularly urged it. I have often found Americans, in particular those engaged in specialized or curious occupations, touchingly ready to take pains in showing and explaining every aspect of their little world to a guest. Perhaps this gives them a fresh interest in work which has become routine.

So I was conducted to the floor below. Four massive bulls were standing in boxes set closely side by side. As soon as they saw the engineer they began to rattle and snort. The inspector reported:

"Super Anxiety the 65th is restless. I think we must give him service today."

The engineer answered coolly: "Yes, I know. Do you suppose I haven't looked at the plan?"

The stalls were of the same fresh-smelling cement as the whole building. They opened onto a small concrete court surrounded by a high gray wall. In the corner of this court a yoke was fixed to a sort of wheel spoke. Here, I was told, the bulls were attached and could trot in a circle once or twice a day between the wall and the house, and back to the wall and again to the house, in order not to lose the use of their muscles.

Now the overseer opened the stable door and jumped aside. The bull plunged heavily forward. There was only one direction for him and only one choice. For he was suspended from a chain fastened to a guiding rail above his head. The rail led out into the fresh air, through a long open passage to something dark waiting at the end of it. Was it a cow? From a distance it appeared to be. As the bull leaped upon the dark something I wondered that there was no sound to be heard except the heavy breathing of the male animal. Suddenly he left off, turned round and trotted slowly back to his pen.

There remained behind a curious thing, which I was now able to look at more closely. It was a hide-covered wire trestle, an artificial cow without a head but with an artificial female sex organ. The bull had leaped upon a dummy, and the extraordinary thing was that this seemed to make no difference to him.

"Formerly we used real cows for the purpose but too much semen was lost that way, and besides, the valuable bull ran the risk of illness," said Mr. Polk. "We saw that the bull could perfectly well be fooled. Very few animals refuse to spring upon our artificial cows."

He brought up to the laboratory a longish black rubber vessel detached from the trestle, shook the semen into a phial and took a slide which he laid under the microscope.

"Excellent," he said, "outstanding quality." He picked up the house telephone and spoke to the attendant downstairs, "Give Anxiety a slap from me on the rear shank."

Now he turned briskly to the index, got out the bull's card, entered a mark on it and began leaving with me for his car, to start on the day's rounds.

"Don't forget your list!" the ill-humored secretary called after him. He turned, took up the sheet of paper and wasted no further glance on anyone in the room.

PART FIVE

Grasping at People

THE CHURCH AND THE
SKYSCRAPER

New York City, New York

"Boom . . . Boom . . . Boom" fell the strokes of the heavy pneumatic hammer. It made the earth tremble beneath us and blotted out the street noises as it struck, struck and struck: like a giant's fist battering at a door.

We stood in the fine white drizzle of building dust and looked on as the church at the corner of Fifth Avenue and Forty-eighth Street trembled and groaned beneath the blows. Suddenly one of the Gothic spires began to move. It looked like an immeasurably bewildered headshake. Then the foreman beside me yelled "STOP!"

The giant did not obey. It stamped on, drunk with its own noise. The strut bowed still further, plunged after a brief hesitation into the boarded-off area surrounded by red flags. And only now the big thing stopped with a wild snort. A workman in blue overalls and a loose colored woolen jacket came up to us and growled: "Tough."

The old St. Nicholas Church was indeed a tough customer. It had held out longer than most New York churches against the advance of the many-storied office buildings, had looked on while right and left steel scaffolding grew higher than the stone spiral of its tower, had clung tightly when the subway tunnels, the mole passages of the sewer system, the narrow-bored passages of the telephone wiring and the electric cable perforated the rock of Manhattan beneath it. But now the game was up. The Last Judgment had struck for the little church.

The doom was not pronounced by angels with fiery swords.

155

The destroyers of the house of God were not even iconoclasts or haters of religion, but the honest paid employees of a demolition firm, the Walsh Wrecking Corporation. They worked at the order of the pious Council of Elders of the Dutch Collegiate Reformed Church, for a fixed fee. Edward R. Walsh, of the board of directors, a man with the figure of a bulldozer and arms like cranes, had come in person to attend the start of the operations. "Nice church," he declared professionally; "all belvedere brownstone. Could have stood up another five hundred years."

But the Council of Elders had decided otherwise. The land, in the heart of New York's most valuable building area, had long been unofficially valued by brokers at four, then six, then finally eight figures. The temptation became overwhelming. The church fathers thought of their not-too-well-filled coffer, they pictured all they could do with the proffered sum. In vain the pastor of St. Nicholas', Dr. Joseph Szoo, fought for his church. He tried to move public opinion to favor the preservation of this peaceful nook of God in the midst of the noisy business world. Protests were advertised in the newspapers, there were meetings and resignations. But in the end it was necessary to submit to the treasurer's arguments. The devil has many names, and in this century he likes to call himself "Mr. Profit" or "Mr. Efficiency." A very good contract was made. On the site of the old church the Sinclair Oil Company building would already be standing the following year: twenty-one stories, all rented in advance, in which, among other things, some popular magazines were to be published, the affairs of a whisky firm conducted, and the complaints in divorce suits prepared.

First the flooring was torn up. Then came the organ pipes. They fell on the naked rock of Manhattan, freed from its light cement cover, with dull growls or loud cries. The stained-glass windows were pierced by beams of the scaffolding. Where the altar had been a rock borer drilled with a diamond point. He was testing the ground so that the future foremen could decide how strong the foundations would have to be to support a skyscraper instead of a church. Urns with ashes were brought out of a vault in the cellar. No one had known of their presence, not even the relatives of these long dead. Three millstones were also found. In the Old World the Dutch, among whom the congregation had originated, had held divine services in a mill. Now their relics, once carried across a wide sea in flight from the persecutors of their religion, were to move again.

"Old Nick" was only an empty frame. And that too would soon be nothing but dust and mortar. Wooden slides were already being built, through which broken fragments dropped noisily into empty trucks. Instruments of destruction bearing the name of "skull crackers" would batter the despoiled, shaken building increasingly day by day.

"I'll need sixty men for ten weeks to bring the church level with the ground," stated Mr. Walsh. "It's all solidly built and we can only work full strength in the hours of light traffic, particularly at night. But this church isn't as hard a job as a number of other churches I've pulled down."

I inquired whether he was a specialist in church demolition.

"No, it's not the sort of work I like to take on," said Mr. Walsh, "and as a matter of fact it's not a very paying job for a wrecker. Practically nothing worth selling at second hand. No steel pillars, few pipes, no bathtubs and almost no radiators. No comfort, no plumbing, no nothing. Just old stuff that may as well go straight to the rubbish heap."

That is where the remains of Old Nick have finally ended. They lie in Secaucus Marsh near New York mixed with the rubble of the Imperial Hotel, which has also had to give way to a new glass and chromium skyscraper.

Not many weeks after the fall of Old Nick I rode in an open transport lift through the red-painted steel framework of the Sinclair Oil Company building which was coming into being. Up there on the small wooden bridges I shook hands with the men who were erecting one of the most modern skyscrapers of Manhattan on the site of the old church.

Skyscraper builders, I have been told, are a very special race.

There are hardly more than five to six hundred workers in this branch and they receive salaries thirty to forty per cent higher than those of other building workers.

Generally they work in gangs of eight. One of these is an apprentice, and although he has the least experience he is at once allowed to do the most dangerous work. That is a sort of admission test. If he is afraid to run along one of the thin steel girders suspended a few hundred feet above ground he will not, in the view of his older colleagues, lose this fear through habit. It is better for him, they believe, to look around for another occupation right away. Should the young man stand the test he soon advances to "spider." One or two years later he becomes "catcher" and has the task of seeing to it, with a pail in his hand, that none of the rivets or other working materials fall down onto the crowded street. Eventually he can rise to be the "gun man" who joins together the steel frame with his riveting hammer.

These gun men have generally passed their first youth. One of those I saw on the scaffolding must surely have been in his middle fifties. He had taken part in the "skyscraper boom" after the First World War when a gigantic new building appeared yearly on the sky line of New York.

"These days," he told me, "it's all child's play. No one builds as high as we used to in the twenties. Then you really needed courage for the job, but now there's nothing much to it. This building will have twenty-one stories. What's that compared to the hundred and two stories of the Empire State? The skyscrapers never properly recovered from the big crisis. Lucky for us specialists that any are being built at all. For a while it looked as if the whole show was over."

He was right. At the beginning of the thirties it really appeared as though the days of the skyscraper were numbered. "They'll die out like mammoths and dinosaurs," claimed one of the leading American architectural journals at the time. "The skyscrapers are monuments of an epoch and a mentality whose end is foreshadowed." This gloomy forecast was made at a moment when half the New York skyscrapers were suddenly standing half empty. During the great boom after the first war ever higher and riskier buildings were piled up—until all at once there was far too much office space on Manhattan, whose bankrupt tenants had left the premises in some cases not by the door but through the window.

"The skyscraper is a superseded form of the overconcentration of economic power," people wrote during the "crisis hang-over." "We shall build no more skyscrapers."

But the skyscrapers survived the crisis. That "overconcentration of economic power," nearly everywhere assailed during the crisis years, not only outlived the first attack of illness but spread to other economic spheres which had not previously been so strongly centralized.

But above all the skyscrapers were rehabilitated by the efficiency experts. They calculated, stop watch in hand, how much time the tenants of the skyscrapers would lose if their offices were spread out horizontally over the whole city and its surroundings instead of being piled vertically on top of one another.

"If you want to launch a new loan to the Kingdom of Norway, for example, you can gather all the people involved around you in the shortest possible time," they told the head of a large banking house who had decided to flee the skyscraper canyons of Wall Street, "but if you transfer your office to the edge of town you'll simply ruin your firm. It would take five times as long for each transaction."

The years in which the owners of one of the largest New York skyscrapers had to have pretended tenants by turning on the electric light on whole floors when it began to be dark soon passed, and again the skyscrapers were sold out down to the last square foot. Office space in New York finally became so scarce that after the end of the Second World War new artificial summits began to mark the city's sky line. Every industry grown big or bigger during the war now wanted its own skyscraper.

The mentality of the tycoons, indeed, has changed. They no longer wish to send their towers higher and higher into the sky for the sake of prestige. They once tended to erect "cathedrals of business," powerful stone pyramids to commemorate their victories and conquests in the field of trust battles and stock-exchange wars. The new generation of big business is less ostentatious and romantic. It prefers to derive satisfaction from the size of its bank balances rather than of its office buildings. It is not the building with the most impressive number of stories that it seeks to erect but the one most economically remunerative.

For it has been calculated that skyscrapers have an economic optimum value. Twenty to thirty and at the very most forty-two stories will pay. Anything that climbs up to sixty, eighty or, indeed, a hundred and two stories becomes too expensive in construction and upkeep to be profitable. So at the close of the Second World War the era began of the "baby skyscrapers," which are less monumental than their predecessors but are felt to be more worth while.

It will be a long time before we again see eccentric figures like the great skyscraper builders of the twenties. There were the four Starrett brothers whose bitterest rival was the fifth brother, who had gone over to another firm.

There was John Jacob Raskob, whose grandfather had emigrated from Gross Littgen in the Eifel in 1846: as a businessman successful and distinguished, as a devout Catholic tireless in the promotion of church affairs; for a time director of E. I. du Pont de Nemours and Company and leading man in General Motors and the Bankers Trust Company of New York.

It was Raskob who, in 1929, first conceived the idea of the Empire State Building. At that time America was at the peak of her postwar prosperity. An ever-increasing number of large firms were coming from other states to set up their main offices at the great money center of New York. The space for new office buildings at the narrow lower end of Manhattan became correspondingly cramped. The city broadened and thrust itself farther uptown toward Central Park.

At that time Raskob used to lunch in the Gentleman's Café of the solid old Hotel Waldorf-Astoria at Thirty-fourth Street. One day it occurred to him to construct a new office building near the two large railway stations of New York, which would surpass all other skyscrapers in size and beauty. He found an estate agent by the name of Kaufmann who was sniffing along the same trail. At once the Du Ponts, who had been looking for investment outlets, were informed of the project and promised support. First the site of the Waldorf-Astoria, then the surrounding properties were obtained in complete secrecy. It was possible to acquire ex-Governor Al Smith, Raskob's political associate, as window dressing, and one day with no great publicity the trip hammers and pickaxes began to attack the dusty splendor of the Waldorf-Astoria. The drawing-room mirrors were sold to provincial hotels, the marble columns sawed to bits, the carpets auctioned. "The end of an era," wrote the New York newspapers when this erstwhile meeting place of the elegant world became nothing but a rubble heap.

Never before had so gigantic a building been erected in so short a time and, moreover, at the traffic center of a city. No single architect and no single building firm could have dealt with this task alone. Committees were formed, a sort of government with a finance minister, a department for underground building work, another for the purchase of raw materials, a third for electrical installations, a fourth for the erection of the steel scaffoldings. The chief executive was Andrew Eken, the head of the building division of Starrett Brothers. He had everything planned in advance for the construction of the then largest building in the world. Every strut, every stone was to be brought and fitted at an appointed date. Every truck with building materials had to time its hour of arrival. If it came only a little too late it might have to wait a week for the next chance to unload.

Even snowstorms, rainy days and dislocations of work were provided for in this complicated and detailed timetable. Only the stock exchange catastrophe of 1929 had, in the fine weather period of 1928, not been foreseen. It threatened to shake the whole complicated financial foundation, put together out of mortgages, credits, shares and expectations of dividends.

But Raskob finally succeeded in having the building proceed in the face of threatening crisis. It was through his efforts that the Empire State Building could be inaugurated on the anticipated date, May 1, 1931. He did not despair when two-thirds of the offices remained vacant and the largest building in the world was mockingly referred to as "the largest ghost city in the world." When the building finally began to pay, from 1941 onward, Raskob retired to his property in Delaware. But his desk on the eightieth floor of the Empire State Building was always kept ready for him. There I met his blonde secretary, who had for months been vainly waiting for one of her employer's rare visits and beguiling the long hours high over the roof tops with the reading of detective stories. Finally Raskob ceased coming altogether, for he had developed a strong aversion to the bustle of the large city. He died in 1950 far from New York and from his skyscraper.

But Andrew Eken, the chief builder, is still alive. I saw him in his office against a background of innumerable windows and the measured zigging lines of his gigantic creations: a friendly, rather tired old man with thin steel-edged spectacles. And he spoke again of his favorite, his problem child, the Empire State. Within the next few days his men were to set up an aerial for television on the highest point of the building. As he spoke of it his gray face began to lighten: "The wind up there," he said, "blows and beats. We wanted to set up a protective scaffolding for the safety of the workmen, but the steel-construction people laughed at us. They'll rope their boys on. If one of them blows down he'll hang on a line like a fish. He may have a scare but he won't be hurt."

The last elevator to which I changed on my ride to the top of the Empire State Building was nearly empty. Only a young couple with a baby were still with me. The door opened for the last time. A bright whitish light streamed in, the sort of light one meets with on mountaintops. We were in the observatory, the highest point to which the public is admitted, and the baby, disturbed in his sleep, gave loud expression to his grief.

A million people yearly visit the observation platform.

Sometimes the sun is shining here while a rain cloud bursts a few flights lower down. Often the "summit" is veiled in mist. Then the visitors are warned on the ground floor that the view today is not clear.

Among these visitors have been Albert Einstein, Arabian princes, English football teams, Russian trade-union delegates, countless loving couples and single visitors. Those for whom a view over mountain ranges of houses seen across two arms of a river is not sufficient can make their own phonograph records in automatic cabins, telephone, or eat hot dogs in the restaurant. It is not advisable to look too long and thoughtfully at the improbable panorama because such starers may be suspected of contemplating suicide by the seven watchers stationed here. In the middle of 1946 this "anti-suicide police" was installed on the platform after seventeen persons had ended their lives in leaps from the highest building in the world. At the end of the war the majority were former soldiers, victims of peace, who no longer wished to live in the disillusioned postwar world. Or bewildered men like the diamond merchant Solomon Rosbach, who, before his jump on May 9, 1946 left a cryptic message: "No above, no below. So I jump." Or the young and beautiful Evelyn McHale who fell down onto the roof of a motorcar and lay there for a while, as on a raised bier, gaped at by thousands of passers-by who happened to be walking through Thirty-fourth Street. "I believe I cannot be a good wife to my fiancée," she wrote before her leap.

Above the public observatory there is a little room on the hundred and second floor where the General Electric Company has been experimenting for years with the phenomena of lightning. For the tip of the building, rising high above the confusion of houses, is a gathering point for electrical discharges. Automatic cameras, installed in neighboring houses, and oscillographs, in the round tower room, register up to eighty strikes a year.

The thought of being torn down into the depths by one of "these loony suicides" is the only thing that sometimes embitters the calling of Ritchie Hart, chief window cleaner at the Empire State. For many years he has had the cleaning of the twenty-four windows on the hundred and second floor entirely to himself. The height—some twelve hundred feet above the earth—does not make him nervous. Whether one falls from the sixth or the hundred and second story makes no great difference, he believes. The only unpleasant features are the sudden incalculable gusts of wind that sometimes bluster round the smooth walls of the tower. Or the sash windows, difficult to open, which occasionally fall shut and cannot be prized up again by the window cleaner suspended outside.

"Then one nearly freezes," says Ritchie, "specially in the morning early when there's no one about but us window cleaners and a couple of charwomen, the thing begins to be ticklish. You call and call but nobody hears you."

All the same Ritchie Hart considers his calling less nerve-racking than that of a coal miner, which he used to be. When he climbs out of the office window, instinctively finds with his shoes the narrow ledge on the outer wall where his feet can gain a hold, hooks in on both sides the leather strap that holds him at the back and begins his work in perfect peace of mind, people who look at him from below hold their breath. "Once when we were newly married my wife brought the lunch parcel I'd forgotten. From the street she saw me hanging up here, and fainted. She's gotten used to the sight since, though."

Hart is a lean, quiet Yankee from Maine with long arms and big feet that are just right for this occupation. He can clean windows as well with his left hand as with his right. Even on icy cold New York winter days when he has to pour alcohol into his pail to keep the water from freezing he works without gloves. He wears a large pair of goggles because the wind blows quantities of sharp soapsuds into his face. Hart's fellow workers, like most of the window cleaners in New York, are of Ukrainian origin. The Ukrainian immigrants, who were the first to undertake this difficult task, have seen to it that their compatriots and descendants have almost a monopoly. The first Ukrainian window cleaners were mainly socialists who had left Czarist Russia on account of their political convictions. This tradition, too, has been maintained. The windows of the skyscrapers, regarded as emblems of American capitalism, are polished daily by these convinced anti-capitalists to a state of brilliant luster.

Few window cleaners look upon their work as dangerous. They scold occasionally because the foot ledges under modern windows are always being made narrower. "Do the architects take us for mountain goats?" they say. Their work is comparatively well paid, their eight-hour day begins at four in the morning and finishes at two in the afternoon. A person who is afraid the first time he goes out of the window is unlikely to lose his fear later on. This was the case with a man Ritchie Hart once took up with him just as a suicide jumped from above. "It was a hell of a business," said Hart; "the fellow came down just between me and the man with me. He had a damned funny expression on his face. Then the wind caught him and carried him right over to the other side of the street, where the Waldorf Cafeteria is. The new man resigned that same morning."

The chief window cleaner claims that he himself never has premonitions of a possible fall. But if you question him closely he admits to being pursued by a curious dream. "I'm hanging up there on the hundred and second floor and some fellow chases me. We rush round and round the tower. God, am I scared! Since then I have a look every morning when I come up in the dark to see whether some loony hasn't hidden there to grab me and pull me with him out of the window."

Such a nightmare is more likely to attack people in the Empire State than in other skyscrapers. The building has the reputation of having a hoodoo on it. The bad luck began with unusually many accidents at the time of construction; then came the financial catastrophe; then the big strike of the elevator operators during which the tenants of the upper floors were temporarily cut off from the world like keepers of lighthouses and the paper, with no charwoman to clear it up, accumulated ankle deep. But the high spot of the "black series" was the peculiar accident of July 28, 1945. It was an unusually foggy day. The employees of the Catholic welfare organization, which had its offices on the seventy-eighth floor, were entirely wrapped in heavy cloud. Suddenly—it must have been a vision of Hell for many a clergyman working there—the walls began to cave in around them, the floor gave way under their feet, immense flames shot from the ceiling. In the lower stories only a powerful jolt was felt; the telephone exchanges were deluged with panicky calls. Was the entire building breaking up? Was there an earthquake? Was the tower of Babel collapsing within itself? A man plunged senseless from the seventy-eighth story in flight from the flames. An elevator, with the operator Betty Oliver inside, crashed when its cable was severed as by a large pair of scissors.

Not until several minutes later was it possible to realize what had happened. A twin-engined Mitchell bomber had lost its way in the fog over the city and run into the skyscraper tower as into a wall of rock, badly damaged two stories and then plunged burning into the canyon of the streets. One of the motors was found half a mile away. Eleven people were killed in this disaster and there was only one witness to tell the tale: a dictaphone roll which continued running. A man's voice could be heard dictating a business letter, his scream of fright quickly drowned by the noise of motors, shrill telephone rings, cries for help. It was a sound picture of the end of a world, the end of a creation as sublime as it was rash. Voices were raised at that time against the construction of new skyscrapers. They were not heard. Skyscrapers are still being built all over America; everything is still being scrapped that stands in the path of their advance.

The man, leaning against the wall opposite the long row of elevator doors in the new Sinclair Oil Company building, is not noticed by the hundreds of people passing in and out. He is not, for that matter, a noticeable type. His suit probably comes from Klein's or Crawford's on Fourteenth Street, a standard model in a greenish-gray standard material. The face of its owner also seems to come off the peg: model "White Collar," medium size. The chin is nearly as energetic as that of the successful executive who at thirty-three has become vice president of the sales division of a large chemical concern. The rimless glasses, together with the bright butterfly bow on the faultless white nylon shirt, announce that he has attended school for at least twelve years and certainly could not yet give up claims to intellectual superiority.

How superior he is to every individual, every secretary and every boss who steps through the doors of this skyscraper today Mr. White Collar alone knows. For he is here to make a survey, a study of the behavior of the genus *Man* in the lobby of the Sinclair Oil building now occupying the site of the former St. Nicholas Church. By profession Mr. White Collar is an industrial engineer. That is his official title. But the elevator staff, who have seen him at work since early morning with a stop watch in one hand and a notebook in the other, have given him a less distinguished name. They call him, with an undertone of hate, "timekeeper," and make all kinds of speculations as to how their future working pace will be affected by what the patient observer is tirelessly noting down.

For the men with the stop watches are highly unpopular among American workers. There is hardly a trade in which they do not from time to time appear, observe, note, observe again, note again. What comes of this is that the norm of production is raised and the job, be it at the turning lathe, typewriter, shop counter or cash desk, develops into a sort of drill in which each movement is calculated in inches and numbers of seconds. The increase in production and timesaving thus achieved, particularly by large enterprises, can make a difference of millions of dollars.

Sometimes the "timekeepers" bring along film cameras and sound-strip instruments. They supplement their own fixed gaze and inquisitive ear with the lens's glass eye and the sensitive electronic vibration, in order to study the person under observation still more carefully later in the dark projection room. The accelerated sound film will then betray every delay in a movement, every uncertainty in a voice, every vacillation, every inefficiency.

But the man leaning against the wall of the skyscraper lobby is observing not the elevator operators but the elevator users, who have not the faintest idea that they are being watched. They do not, in any case, interest the timekeeper as individuals, only as anonymous particles of a mass which flows into the skyscraper and is sucked up or discharged by the tube system of the elevators. The timekeeper wishes to know when this flow is at its maximum, when at its minimum. When is the traffic circulation overburdened? When do jams, inconveniences, irritations occur because the waiting time in front of the elevators is too long? It takes seventeen seconds, the man with the stop watch has noted, for the average man to press the button for the second time. He will bear it quietly for up to thirty seconds, but by the end of thirty-five seconds patience is bursting, he becomes annoyed, complains of the poor service, plays with the thought of perhaps going away altogether. "I've been standing here five minutes!" he throws at the elevator operator. Our timekeeper knows that it was only one minute. But he also knows that something must be done not to put the visitors out of humor, or else the businesses will suffer. Several tenants are already demanding a reduction of the high rental on the grounds of inadequate elevator service.

That the elevators in the Sinclair Oil Company building are insufficient is not the fault of the architects who planned it. They had provided just as much conveyance as was needed to take care of the "vertical traffic" without friction. But the management, pressed by applicants, had squeezed more tenants into the available room than had been reckoned with. This feat was made possible by an efficiency expert who practiced all kinds of space-saving sorcery at the last moment, with new subdivisions between the offices, and out of an average of two suites hurriedly produced three. In this way the total of the rent receipts was increased by more than twenty-five per cent—naturally at the expense of the general comfort.

Now unavoidable signs of friction have appeared. But the management of the building does not despair. It has called in a second efficiency expert (from the same firm, by the way), who, through clever manipulation, is to try, with time, to smooth the difficulties caused by his colleague's juggling with space. That is the sorcerer's multiplication table of efficiency, which is always trying with new tricks to rescue what it has ruined—in the end, naturally, at the expense of everybody's nerves.

This task has fallen to Mr. White Collar. His recommendations will determine whether the discomfort and the demands for reduced rentals can be ended without giving up the profitable overfilling of the building.

There is no question of accelerating the speed by installing faster elevators. The building possesses the fastest possible "express elevators" which open automatically, stop automatically at the command of their "selectomaton"—a primitive electronic brain—"take note of" every signal on every floor and in case of being full pass it on to another elevator.

Therefore a different method of regulating traffic must be found in the skillful guidance of the occupants and visitors of the building. The "timekeeper" will recommend that two wholesale firms, renting an upper story apiece, stagger their opening, lunch and closing hours "in their own interest," so that the peak of the traffic curve may be slightly leveled. He will work out a six-point timetable, calculated in seconds. But first of all the expert, who has an ever-flowing mass of humanity to deal with, will recommend the adjustment of the revolving doors so that they will be harder to push. In this way the flow of the multitude will be substantially retarded at the entrance.

Mr. White Collar will then recommend the establishment of an information desk directly opposite the entrance. About a third of the passers-by, even if they already know the office they are going to, will wish to fortify their certainty that they have not forgotten the floor and room number. In this way the visitor gains the impression that he is being given service, not guessing that the actual purpose of the helpfulness is inconspicuously to impede him in his effort to precipitate himself upon the elevators. It is furthermore important, the timekeeper believes, to keep one elevator always open for new arrivals. The stop watch, coupled with observation, reveals that the "phase of impatience" sets in much later if the visitor, instead of standing before a shut door, is already waiting inside the lift. He then has the feeling that something is being done for him. The main thing is for him to be able to indulge in this illusion.

All this I learned from Mr. White Collar himself when I visited the completed and opened Sinclair Oil Company building to see what had become of the place where the St. Nicholas Church had stood.

I rode up and down a few times in the elevator and thought nostalgically of my ride in the airy steel scaffolding of the same building. Then I sent in my name to the manager and learned that for two years to come there was not one office to be had in this most modern of New York buildings. "It's a big success," he said. The only trouble was the overpopulation of the all-too-popular building. But that was being remedied. Thus I came to know the time taker who reckons in seconds and minutes in the place where only two years earlier the joys of eternity were being preached.

ROBOTS IN THE OFFICE

Endicott, New York

WHEN the famous general to whom New York offered a public reception had passed through the narrow, winding defile of lower Broadway, the road and pavements were covered in paper a foot deep which had been snowed down from the top stories onto the homecomer and his motor escort. I inspected a few of these flakes which had clung to my hair, suit and shoes: scraps of bills, requests for payment, business orders, inventories. Here was a scrap of an order for textiles from Japan, there the last sentences of a warning note, and again and again numbers. Four-figure, five-figure, six-figure sums—shadows of yesterday's deals, of past transactions.

In other countries returning warriors are strewn with flowers. To me this ovation of New York to the proconsul of American influence returning from the distant East seemed more meaningful and seasonable. For these delicate lines on white, blue, green and pink paper were the true symbol of the power in whose name the general had fought, conquered and governed. The fragments of account statements and orders for delivery which fluttered onto his military cap and the shoulders of his uniform had more genuine significance than the golden stars which proclaimed his rank.

For the power today dwells in office buildings, not in houses of representatives nor even in council rooms. It is from the office that life and work are directed, to a degree formerly unheard of. From the gigantic stone honeycombs in which desk stands beside desk a hundredfold, and then twenty to eighty times desk stands over desk, the abundance of products, the mass of producers and consumers, is guided on long paper reins. The American sociologist, C. W. Mills, writes strikingly about the new seat of power in bureaucratically centralized America: "The office is the invisible hand. . . . The thousand rules that you yourself never made, applied to you by a thousand people you have never seen and never will see."

It is often assumed that the industrial revolution occurs only in laboratories and factories. One forgets too easily that the general staff of this revolution resides in the offices. Without the increasingly extensive and complicated activities of private and public organizations, the industrial revolution would long since have come to a stop or been buried in the ruins of its own too highly placed hopes. Should an opponent wish to strike a grave blow at America's gigantic industrial production he would obtain the quickest results if he aimed at its head, its great office quarters.

Until the turn of the century, and even up to the First World War, private and public bureaucracies played a far smaller role in the United States than in European officialdom. Two wars, an important economic crisis and an unpredictably long "cold war" of world-wide dimensions have reversed the situation. The U.S.A. has become more bureaucratic than most European countries.

This is due not only to increased state intervention in economic and private affairs, but at least as much to the efforts of the powerful public corporations to leave as little as possible to chance. Planning down to the smallest detail, control of each labor process, the abolition of all possible waste of time, characterize the American earning system. The same smooth functioning is required of the man as of the machine. "Efficiency" has grown more important in the working world than freedom.

Although industry and the state have done all in their power to reduce the paper work, this burden and with it the number of office employees has been growing year by year. Production planning, inventory controls, factory organization, marketing, complicated methods of financing, refinements of statistics and, in addition to these, tax demands, trade-union problems, deductions for social insurances, proposals for the allotment of raw materials and state subsidies—all these have yearly been piling up work for office staff. From 1900 to 1950 the number of white collar workers has multiplied by eight. In the middle of the century eight million American men and women were employed in offices. In factories there was one clerical worker to every four other workmen.

In the decade between 1935 and 1945 the situation in some quarters reached a crisis. Bookkeepers were reckoning too slowly and inaccurately for the exigencies of large businesses, banks and government offices. These concerns could not keep up with their growth. They began to lose control over their own extended and complicated operations, the right hand no longer knew what the left was doing. The largest administrative business of all, the state, "mislaid" entire warehouses through erroneous entries, "forgot" an arsenal and purchased things of which it had long had a surplus. All because there was no longer an over-all view.

The watchword of America had always been: "Bigger and bigger!" Now came the realization that bigness could become a curse, that in economy as in public life it was no occasion for pride but rather one for self-criticism, no sign of untrammeled growth but a sickly excrescence. Between 1930 and 1940 it was often said that government and industry would have to bring their functions back into humanly containable proportions. Large concerns began to split up their spheres of power and the movement toward increasing monopoly was beginning to be voluntarily curbed on the ground of impracticability.

But at that point technique came to the rescue of the managements of mammoth undertakings and with one stroke put an end to the contemplated decentralization. There appeared, during the Second World War, a new type of office machine—at first only in military establishments, later on the open market—able to make in one hour calculations on which dozens of statisticians would have had to spend hundreds of hours. They shoveled the

avalanches of paper off the desks, devouring their way through
previously unconquerable mountains of numbers and letters as
playfully as the great road-building machines eat up sand and
stone: the road to control of more men and more property in
fewer hands was again open. By means of the "mechanical brain,"
the Leviathan State and the Leviathan Big Business were once
again saved.

Endicott—that is the name of a quiet little town in the green
Susquehanna Valley, a couple of hundred miles to the west of
Manhattan and at present hardly known to the world. But in
the course of the next decade Endicott will probably become as
famous as the motor town of Detroit. For Endicott has been the
first to produce mechanical brains in quantity and has thereby
become the starting point of a development which may well have
consequences at least as far-reaching as the mass production of
automobiles. From Endicott the machine penetrates into the
realm of thought. It is able to carry out nearly every kind of
straightforward logical thinking operation with superhuman
speed. Thus on the one hand it simplifies many time-consuming
routine operations, but on the other seduces its human masters
into posing only such problems as may be solved with the help
of the unimaginative but extraordinarily thorough mechanical
brain. As a driver keeps to the smooth, straight highways on
which his car travels easily and avoids the rough cross-country
roads, the "thinking machine" draws its user away from difficult
ground and banishes him to the calculable main roads of the
spirit.

Like Detroit, which in its early stages was dominated by the
eccentric, autocratic figure of Henry Ford, Endicott, the "town of
the office machine," also stands in the shadow of a single man:
Thomas J. Watson. His portrait, the head of a friendly elderly
man with a priestly smile on the thin lips, and a gleaming white
collar like a halo that has fallen down, hangs in hundreds of rooms
inside and outside the factory. Even oftener than his portrait one
finds in monumental capital letters the master's motto: THINK.

THINK gleams over every door, leaps at you from every wall. It is a command without an exclamation mark: THINK. The omnipresent imperative is planted in red tulips on green turf, chiseled in stone or marble, cast in bronze, embroidered on material, burned into the night in light-writing: THINK . . . THINK . . . THINK . . . One begins by hating the command for its importunity and ends by not noticing it at all. THINK becomes as void of meaning as "Good morning."

Before a visitor has time for reflection, the ready-made answers are provided for him with the speed of office machines. "I AM THE MOST SATISFIED MANAGER," purrs an executive faultlessly clothed in the same high collar and stiff business uniform as his chief. "WE ARE THE HAPPIEST COMMERCIAL REPRESENTATIVES," falls from the lips of the salesmen. "WE ARE THE HAPPIEST WORKERS," say, at the lightest tap, the freshly shaven gentlemen and pleasantly smiling girls who, surrounded by charming colors, are assembling robots out of electric parts to the sound of soft automatic music.

The person to be thanked for this state of bliss is revealed in the firm's songbook which every "helper"—for here there are officially no chiefs, no employees and laborers—possesses, as well as the memorandum book with the gold-embossed motto THINK. "You're our leader fine," it says in Company Song No. 7. "By him we're all inspired . . ." affirms the refrain of Song No. 5. "We sing our praise from the depths of our hearts . . ." says another song dedicated to the Leader which resounds at the Monday evening meeting—similar to a religious service—for inner and outer improvement.

Mr. Watson himself receives these honors with a modesty in keeping with a storybook figure. He too would like to be just a simple salesman, he allows it to be known; all the same he has no objection if, in the magazines and brochures brought out by his company for the edification of the "helpers" and the heathen world around them, he is referred to as the "greatest SALESMAN in the Universe." From these publications we learn that at bottom Columbus too was only a salesman. He sold his Queen the idea of discovering America and thus opened up for the Spanish

Crown a rich new territory which Spain failed to hold merely because she was unaware of another utterance of Mr. Watson's,
which runs: "He who is not always getting better stops being
good."

Thomas Watson began his career as salesman of pianos, organs
and sewing machines, worked his way up to being chief salesman
of the National Cash Register Company, whose automatic cash
registers had begun their triumphal progress, and was appointed
in 1914 to direct a small, rather down-at-heel concern dealing
mainly in stop watches. The holy book of Mr. Watson's helpers,
his collection of speeches, articles and maxims, bearing the awe-
inspiring title *Men-Minutes-Money,* contains the "pep talk" with
which the Leader, shortly after taking over the business in 1915,
raised the fallen hopes of his new collaborators. "You've got
enough talent here to develop a business many times as big
as this. . . . I don't yet know where the talent is but I do know
it exists," proclaimed Mr. Watson. One of his closest collaborators
praised this speech one day at the New York World's Fair as "the
turning point of human development."

Mr. Watson has increased the gross earnings of the firm, which
in 1914 showed a profit of half a million dollars a year, to 8.6
million dollars in 1938 and 28.1 million dollars in 1950. The
number of employees grew, under the Leader's wise guidance,
from 235 to 30,000 (branches in 79 countries) and his own
sales commission on the current turnover to thousands of dollars
a day plus an ever-larger share, rising to millions, of the capital
stock. But the chief instrument of this "wonderful development" was a little rectangular card with longish holes.

Among the machines of the concern taken over by Mr. Watson
was a clumsy affair disparagingly referred to by the other directors
as "the statistical piano" because of its outward resemblance to a
Pianola. Its Austrian inventor, Dr. Hermann Hollerith, had originally built it in 1886 for the American census authorities. Its
principle consisted in stamping certain simple types of information
in the form of perforations on cardboard squares. If these cards

ran between a series of small electrically charged metal brushes, wherever the brushes made contact through a hole it closed an electric circuit, which set into motion an adding machine and an automatic typewriter.

It was incontestably a service on Mr. Watson's part to have discovered in this "stepchild" the talent he had hoped to find. With the help of scientists and engineers he enriched and refined the cardboard-hole language to such a degree that it is now able not only to express and combine hundreds of different meanings, but to do so with a speed far beyond the capacity of the human brain. One of his machines is able in a single second to do 2,174 additions or subtractions, 79 multiplications and 65 divisions of five-figure numbers. A sorting machine arranges 27,000 perforated card-index sheets an hour in alphabetic, geographic or any other prearranged order.

What the office robots from Mr. Watson's factory can do I learned in a propaganda pamphlet issued by the firm in conjunction with a large weekly magazine. In the subscription section the lively little folk are described at work:

Punch. His name is Punch. He has a human servant who taps out on a keyboard all important information concerning each subscriber, in accordance with a pre-established numerical code. For every figure, Punch makes a rectangular hole in a particular spot on a card. The card is filed with millions of others. When all information concerning subscribers has been taken down in this form, other machines can find, sort and put it away, multiply it and get it back again. Of course, if the servant gives Punch the wrong numbers, he will punch the wrong holes. And that could lead to great confusion if he did not have the following brother.

The Eye. The eye bears a strong outward resemblance to Punch, but his work is very different. If a hole is punched in the wrong place the Eye observes the mistake immediately. He is uncannily precise. He searchingly scans every newly punched card and should a perforation be missing from a place where it ought to be found, gives a dark red stop signal. His servant sees the signal and removes the faulty card.

Sorter. This gifted geographer knows all countries and cities. He has a superlative sense of order. After the subscribers' cards have been punched and tested they lie in a jumble like the mail when it has just been delivered. Sorter takes up a pile of cards and runs through them. As he feels the perforations he is able to sort them out in alphabetic as well as in geographic order.

Choosy. Choosy can pick the card of each subscriber with the greatest speed out of a heap of thousands and also return it to the exact spot where he found it.

The Hen. She would not be here if only a single original card were needed. But we require duplicates for statistical and other purposes. The Hen hatches them in her quiet way.

Tabby. Tabby is a machine which uses one of the two cards hatched by The Hen. She feels the holes in the cards and transfers them by means of a sort of typewriter into letters and numbers, for example names and addresses.

Should these friendly robots by any chance make a mistake because one of their screws is loose, strange phenomena come to pass, straight out of a machine-age fairy tale. One day, for instance, thousands of copies of the same pictorial magazine stacked themselves before the door of a farmer in a remote part of the United States because a robot, in addressing envelopes, had become stuck at his name and written it over and over again.

But these are exceptions. In general, Mr. Watson's docile machines are highly attentive, reliable and punctual. They take inventories, draw up balances, calculate betting odds and insurance risks, compile sales statistics, trade-union contributions and wage deductions. They have become the indispensable helpers in matters of tax, insurance and banking. And these are merely elementary office robots. In Mr. Watson's laboratory electronic brains are being evolved which will reach far greater speeds in the hole language, in response to the slightest variation of electric current. For it seems that the punched-card language is being outstripped by newer creations, relegated to the status of an old language and gradually superseded by more advanced forms of expression. A competitor of Watson's, for example, instead of the cards with holes, uses the magnetic sound strip developed in Germany, which can record, on a five-hundred-meter coil in the form of tiny magnetic points, as much information as the Endicott machines produce on twenty thousand cards.

So far the most highly bred thinking machines are monopolized by the state and the Armed Forces, but other moderately intelligent electronic brains (together with additional receiving and communicating organs costing between 50,000 and 500,000 dollars) are available for general office use. They are able not only to carry out nearly every arithmetical operation with lightning speed, but also to compare thousands of pieces of information in their "memory," to retain them and to find them again on call in a split second and in the right sequence. The organs of communication, which translate the machine language back into ours, are not yet as competent as those of thought and memory, but have developed sufficiently for one firm to have produced a communicating machine printing 24,000 letters or numbers per minute; another has announced a machine capable of writing a thousand lines in sixty seconds.

But even such performances are surpassed by the "charactron" of the aircraft firm Convair (otherwise specializing in the production of long-range bombers)—a sort of television set which receives ten thousand electronic impulses per second, lets them run over a built-in number-and-letter disk and then presents them on the screen in correct intelligible order. The photograph of the thousands of microscopic letters on the screen is taken by a new ultra-fast process, xerography, immediately transferred onto paper and may then be read with a strong magnifying glass.

Mr. Watson and other thinking-machine producers declare: "Our machines free the human spirit by relieving it of routine labor. Time is gained in this way for creative intellectual work." Similar promises were made when the first big machines for the conquest of physical drudgery appeared. It was claimed that man would be freed from the fetters of labor. But in reality only the nature of the labor changed. The working man of today has less need to exert his muscles, but in dealing with the mechanical slaves his nerves and spirit are put to new and severe tests. The work, in changing its character, lost its personality and dignity. In the place of the hand worker appeared the factory laborer, whose special knowledge was simpler and more easily acquired.

A similar evolution is taking place in American offices. They are being filled by a new type of employee. Instead of trained accountants, statisticians and auditors who were required until recently to have a university education, we find office-machine "operators" whose preparatory training is entirely different. Above all, they must have technical routine and mechanical skill. This means that the boundary between factory and office is becoming fluid. There is no reason why a man who operates a metal-stamping machine in the factory should not handle an office machine with equal skill. The efficiency experts, too, have been taken over from the factories. They have introduced the conveyer-belt system into the office, so that the work is divided up into as many single manipulations as possible and "flows" from specialist to specialist.

Thus incoming letters in mail-order or insurance houses are opened at the beginning of the "production line" by the automatic letter opener, brought on a conveyer belt to the sorting clerk (who has the automatic sorter look for the suitable perforated standard answer and the already-stamped address card of the writer), then passes these cards on to the tabulator, which writes the routine answer according to the instructions of the card fifteen times faster (by printing whole lines at a single stroke) than a typewriter would be able to do. The automatic signature machine, the apparatus for putting the letter into an envelope and the stamping and sealing machines complete the operation.

I looked at several of these large offices, which would be better described as letter and number factories. Most impressive was the gigantic building of a large insurance company in Newark, New Jersey, where 4,500 employees were handling the policies of nearly ten million clients on twenty stories connected by vertical conveyer belts. In this task they had the assistance, so the manager told me, of no fewer than 4,500 office machines of the most varied types.

A glance at the government offices for census taking and social security gave me a still clearer presentiment of the office of the future. The large halls, outwardly barely distinguishable from factory workrooms, were filled with the whirring and clicking of the various finding, sorting and writing machines. Along the walls, ceiling high with green filing cabinets, slid ladders on which civil servants worked their way from drawer to drawer, from dossier to dossier. In this way the census-taking can prepare statistical information in a few months concerning a hundred and fifty million Americans, whose individual characteristics have been compressed into numbers for the purpose, and the social security services can administer ninety-three million files, of which 750,000 are dealt with daily.

The bugbear of these large offices is the client or citizen with particular desires. For him no standard answer can be conjured ready-made from the punching machine and the tabulator; he requires personal judgment by a human brain and an individual answer by a flesh-and-blood secretary. At Sears, Roebuck, the famous Chicago mail-order house which has to handle as much post daily as a city of several hundred thousand inhabitants, a lady who was showing me through the "correspondence factory" told me: "When a customer instead of keeping to the catalogue number asks particular questions or expresses particular wishes, he is no longer profitable to us; for he is demanding special attention which calls for the outlay of special labor."

I asked how many such difficult customers the mail-order house was called upon to serve, and she answered with a satisfied sigh, "Thank God, fewer than one per cent."

So far, of course, only businesses dealing in routine work on a very large scale can afford complete mechanization. But just as the manufacturing concerns, by simplifying and standardizing their processes, gradually forced the firms of artisans to transform themselves into factories, so every American office, in order to meet competition, must try to follow the new trend and simplify its operations.

One firm after another engages "method analysts," "system engineers," or "scientific managers," to rationalize its offices.

At first the reorganizer, known where possible only to the management and represented to the personnel as a fellow worker, will study the outmoded methods. He notes that for the taking and delivery of orders there is too much movement from desk to desk. He soon establishes how much time is wasted in private chat, finds that secretaries called to take dictation are kept sitting about waiting for a chief who is not ready for them, that stenographers spend too much time at the typewriter in preparing letters. He knows that a good part of these letters could be tapped out on automatic machines if unproductive particulars such as personal greetings were to be omitted and everyone sent the same letter with only the insertion of the individual name supplying a "personal note."

First the "methods analyst" will have the outer aspect of the establishment altered. About three-quarters of the private offices are done away with, walls and doors disappear and are replaced by a single large workroom, with all desks in the open, or at most with walls halfway up. In this way space is saved, continuous observation of the course of the work is made possible, the flow of individual documents from desk to desk accelerated. An average standard quantity of work, reckoned with a stop watch after each manipulation, is established so that in future there will be no time for private telephone calls and conversation, overlong absences from the place of work or similar "waste of minutes and hours belonging to the employer."

Above all, a thorough reorganization ensures that each employee is continually provided with sufficient work. Letters which cannot be dealt with by the manifolding process are, when possible, not personally dictated to the stenographer but come to her over the sound-strip player, the dictaphone or from the "dictation central," which is switched on by way of the house telephone. The "boss," become invisible, is a voice dictating memoranda which remain meaningless to the secretary who happens to be at his disposal. It is, however, recommended in the interest of output that a friendly "Good morning, Miss" on the sound roll should precede the dictation and a "Thank you, Miss" follow it.

Lunch periods are staggered so as not to cause a break in the routine. Coffee automats and snack bars in the building accelerate the process of taking nourishment.

"This reform has been long overdue," I was told by a scientific manager who showed me the world of office robots. "In the last hundred years the dollar productivity of factory workers has risen by 1,400 per cent, the productive capacity of the office worker by 40 per cent at most. We are merely at the beginning of a far-reaching standardization, mechanization and speeding up of office work. Today, for example, the average worker in the chemical industry has twenty thousand dollars' worth of machinery at his disposal, but the American office worker averages one thousand only. Just think of the possibilities."

"Think. . . ."

"THINK, THINK, THINK," the machines clicked and clattered. I tried to think, my brain hummed and rattled, the cells tried to copy the electronic wires; the neurons flipped and flapped under the strain. But the result aimed at by Mr. Watson was not produced. Only over and over again melancholy visions of pale, silent people standing submissively before exorbitantly active metal boxes and staring with an effort into the will-o'-the-wisp aggregates of wire.

Well—I suppose I must have been wrongly punched.

WORLD WITHOUT WALLS

Detroit, Michigan

AN EDITOR of *Ammunition,* a magazine published by the International Union of Automobile Workers, made the sharpest criticism I have yet heard of certain aspects of industrial psychology. He said to me: "During the war a 'soul engineer' in a factory whose men we organize asked them whom they hated most. At that time our adversaries naturally came first. If that man were to put the question today he would probably find that the leader in such an unpopularity contest was himself; the 'deep psychology' with which the human-relations programs are honoring us has become simply a new name for spying, a new way of driving and oppressing."

This prejudice is by no means universal. Many trade-unionists are entirely in sympathy wih the efforts of the industrial psychologists. They take exception only when the new techniques of soul cure are misused. But that, they say, unfortunately occurs too often.

Perhaps a more eloquent complaint was one I heard from a man at the employing end, Mr. L., the personnel chief of a motor-parts factory. "Some of the things you'll see in my department will astonish and perhaps alarm you. They do me too." These were his surprising words when I handed him my letter of introduction from a close friend of his.

"I am not altogether blameless myself," he admitted. "It was I who first brought these Messrs. 'Soul Bunglers' and their assistants into the works. I had a great respect for science and hoped

185

to accomplish something genuinely helpful to our people. But what came of it? A sniffing around and an agitation, a silly fooling with questionnaires, statistics and dozens of tests. And in return there's not a trace of healthy human understanding left. On paper the production in our factory seems to have risen through these methods. Despite the figures, I doubt it. But even if it were so, the price we pay is too high. Our factory has become a world without walls, without respect for individuality, without regard for private life. Why don't I draw the conclusion and leave? You ought to be able to figure that out without much psychology. I'm over fifty."

With these words, Mr. L. sent me to Mr. H., who, although he nominally works under the chief who views the new methods with horror, has in actual fact the final say in the personnel department. H., a man of about forty, has the smooth porcelain face and courteous manners of the intelligent middle-grade general staff officer, a type one comes across on subcommittees of the Joint Chiefs of Staff in Washington.

H., as he told me, discovered his calling to personnel management when he was in the Army. Driven more or less by chance into a department that used psychological tests to discover the particular aptitudes of recruits and placed them accordingly, he became, when the war was over, a specialist in choice and guidance of personnel.

Even at first glance his office resembles a laboratory. The walls are papered with colored charts, complicated statistical exhibits and graphic curves which look like illustrations of the quantum theory. In these psychographs, productometers, motive profiles, sociograms and communication charts, each worker appears as a fractional number—a decimal part of a total sum.

"The great new development in our field," affirms Mr. H., "is the inclusion of the complete personality of the employee in our evaluations. The theory and practice of scientific management have made considerable strides in the past fifteen years. Former tests contented themselves with noting the surface aspects of the candidate, such as mental reaction and signs of physical skill. Today with the help of personality tests we try to look deeper into the motives of our people. How is their emotional stability? Are they honest? Are they loyal? Do they get on with their fellow workers? What is the state of their private life? Are they married? Have they sex problems? Do they spend their money easily? What is their relationship with their parents? What with their children? Have they got inhibitions? Are they aggressive?

"Each of our employees is appraised according to forty personality traits, beginning with his upbringing, continuing through his capacity for remembering names, on to his political orientation. We don't, of course, wish to exert any direct influence on his political opinions, but as an expression of his personality, these, too, seem implicitly important and informative."

"These tests must be very long and expensive," I interposed.

Mr. H. was not of that opinion. Actually, he said, they saved the firm substantial sums. To put the wrong man in the wrong place, to give responsibility to a person incapable of taking it— these were the things that really cost money. According to his own calculations—he had splendidly illustrated memoranda on the subject to show me—the firm had saved 14.3 per cent in the past year on repairs alone because more carefully chosen people operated the machines. "A single workman can cost us thousands of dollars in damages through a mistake in the handling of a valuable machine. We invest two thousand dollars' worth of instruction in each new worker and see no point in losing it simply because we haven't adequately tested the man's character before engaging him. One single foreman who lets his childish aggressions react on the workers under him can release all sorts of protest responses, which then appear in the form of five-figure losses in the production statistics."

H. proudly showed me the interview rooms in which people seeking jobs were interrogated, given forms to fill in or watched by a tester for their reactions to certain psychological tables. With naïve pride he showed me the files kept in connection with everyone holding or aspiring to a post. There was the information of a local credit office regarding his financial circumstances, reports of his teachers and former chiefs, reports of a detective agency about his private life.

"We leave nothing to chance," said Mr. H., "and we've been proved right."

At all events, this system of "personal weighing" introduced into the firm under his guidance still held, he regretfully admitted, a large gap. "What's the use of all the tests for our lower and middle-grade employees if we, the managers, don't submit ourselves to equally severe ones?" he asked. "Something must and will be altered here. Capability must be the decisive factor in leadership. Not influence or seniority. There are any number of firms which do put their leading people through such tests and have thereby lopped off a great deal of deadwood. Well, one can't have everything right away. . . ." He looked me in the face with an air of aggressive self-consciousness and I guessed at once what he had in mind. Over the head of his superior, Mr. L., the guillotine of personality tests was already suspended.

Advocates of industrial psychology can produce a number of strong arguments for increased psychological penetration of the working world. They believe that the advantages to be gained by probing deeply into personality and private life far outweigh the disadvantages. The people who are tested, they say, are themselves generally grateful for having been prevented from taking up posts they would have been unable to fill. At the same time the continual observation of all employees makes possible the speedier advancement of many a gifted person who would formerly have remained unnoticed.

But in practice, many cases contradict this friendly picture. Since it is a matter of mass choice, the tests are apt to be applied hurriedly, superficially and mechanically. Only too often distorted results are produced and the fate of a capable person endangered by the faulty inferences of a soul engineer with too much work piled on his desk. Despite such errors, which no one denies, American industry keeps to its new system of psychological choice and guidance because, as the personnel chief of a California airplane factory told me, there is no other feasible standard for allotting posts.

"What could we go by otherwise?" he asked. "Hundreds of people about whom we know nothing come into my department in the course of a month asking for employment. When the factories were small and the job seekers came chiefly from the neighborhood, it was easy to dispense with tests. One knew his neighbors, friends, teachers, former employers. But nowadays people travel thousands of miles to find work in a region that suits them. Look at today's application list alone: a man from Vermont, another from Arkansas, a third from Chicago, a fourth from Portland. We can't, really, rely altogether on their word."

An assiduous young psychologist in General Motors who looks after about two hundred thousand people defended the system as follows: "Our concerns have grown to such dimensions that the relationship between the upper and middle ranks and the mass of workers has naturally become less familiar than formerly. In a little business of about a hundred men the chief used to know his people and the people knew each other fairly well. It was easy then to find out which people deserved advancement or a rise in wages. The psychological test is unhappily a necessary substitute for years of close acquaintance. Now we are obliged to conduct mass interrogations regularly, if only to be able to ascertain the general mood in the works."

One of the main difficulties in the way of a fair application of psychological tests is the scarcity of trained psychologists. In 1950, when thousands of firms were demanding the help of soul engineers, there were only three hundred qualified industrial psychologists in existence. Therefore, only the largest firms can, for the present, maintain house psychologists. The others must have recourse to special concerns, such as the Psychological Corporation of New York, thoroughly serious firms, in the midst of the many spurious ones that have followed the trend and plunged into the tempting business of soul guidance.

The fees demanded by the psychological advisory firms are high They are generally consulted, for the first time, when strong signs of social unrest appear in some part of a factory organism. A sudden fall in the production figures not to be accounted for by technical deficiencies, an unusual accumulation of defective products, quarrels in one or more departments and threats of strike are usually the occasion.

The Psychological Corporation, when the alarm is given, moves in at once with its specialists and the whole bag of tricks for the investigation of psychological unrest. The inevitable questionnaires are distributed, personal interviews held with the staff of the business from top to bottom, and on occasion, if simple methods prove inadequate, microphones concealed here and there for the reception of "candid reactions"—that is, expressions of the employees not intended for the ears of the observers.

The diagnosis reached through the investigation, if the business is very large, is obtained by the collation of the facts according to a definite system, stamping on perforated cards and calculations of the average value. The ostensible mood can then be exactly stated in percentages. Such a "report on mood," regarded as a model in professional circles, was made, for example, on behalf of General Motors, on the strength of over a hundred thousand depositions. In order to disguise the true purpose the interrogation was camouflaged as a prize essay; valuable awards in the form of automobiles were offered for the best answers to the question "Why I like my job."

When a firm of psychological advisers has made its report and pointed out ways to a psychological cure, it does not fail to recommend regular psychological guidance as a prescription for prevention of further difficulties and to offer its own services in this respect at a reduced subscription price.

Such a service comprises a test program to eliminate from the start all possible troublemakers and failures among the prospective employees; secondly, comes a "merit rating" program which again scrutinizes the employees and establishes their capacities at regular intervals, considering whether a man is under- or overpaid, whether he ought to be dismissed or promoted; finally, a "morale-building" program, which is responsible for the maintenance of a good mood and working spirit in the business.

If the first psychological "emergency treatment" has been successful, there is every chance that the direction of a business with a modern outlook will secure the permanent collaboration of a firm of soul engineers, especially one which can prove, by application of practical psychology on its own behalf, that its services will cost the client practically nothing since they can be deducted from income tax. In this way the firm of Rohrer, Hibler and Replogle, founded in Chicago in 1945 by the legal psychologist Perry L. Rohrer, acquired one hundred and seventy-five permanent clients in the course of five years. Its specialty is the "development of suitable manager material." First, one of the firm's eighteen qualified psychologists is commissioned to make a series of quick analyses. He maps out, in a few sittings, an exact personal-development history of every man in a responsible position, puts the patient through a series of deep psychological tests and then tries to rebuild him by a lightning treatment on the basis of his acquired experiences. Professional psychologists would probably not think much of the seriousness of these soul treatments if they were told that the conferences between manager and industrial psychologist often take place "during a game of golf or over a glass of beer."

Individual treatment of this sort is too expensive for middle-size businesses. In firms of this class the technique of the group interview is practiced with considerable success. Eight or ten candidates for employment or promotion are brought together in the same room. They are given a general discussion theme closely connected with their work—in an airplane concern, for example, "The advantages and disadvantages of air-freight traffic"—and left to themselves for a prearranged period of generally about an hour. But only in appearance, for at least three observers belonging to the advisory firm are listening to the debates and marking each candidate according to various criteria: Is he too aggressive?

Is he too passive? Is he convincing? Amiable? Does he have personal magnetism? Capacities of leadership? Is he patient or does he easily become irritable?

"The ideal arrangement for such a group interview," writes Harold Fields, one of the testers in the employ of the city of New York, "is a room in which the candidates sit around a table. The walls are of glass, transparent from the outside and like a mirror on the inside. Behind them sits the invisible testing committee. Openings in the wall make it possible to hear what is being said in the room."

The so-called self-valuation techniques have also begun to find favor. Employees who work in the same group are provided with questionnaires in which they are requested to state in confidence to the soul engineer their opinion of their nearest fellow worker. In this way the psychological examiner is said to obtain an exact picture of the "social build-up of the group." He can then, for example, remove a particular harmful element from this body and introduce instead an active optimistic element.

While the participants in such interviews at least know that they are being watched and appraised, this is not true in the case of many of the newer psychological screenings. Sales personnel in department stores and shops are regularly examined for their abilities by testers of the Willmark Corporation who pose as customers. These investigators, to make the deception complete, go to the length of purchasing wares which are later returned to the firm. A report on each sales person is prepared on a form, stating among other things whether he has been friendly or sullen, whether he tried, by suggestive sales technique, to encourage the customer to buy more, whether he kept the disciplinary rules of the business, how he took leave of the customer. It is a matter of pride with the Willmark Service System and its thirty-three branches all over America that virtually none of its sales analysts is ever unmasked by one of his victims.

Some firms use the system of keeping an applicant waiting at length in an anteroom while they have him watched through television cameras or simply by a schooled secretary. Before the man has even had a chance to speak with the chief of personnel he has been unwittingly judged and condemned. For they believe it possible to determine by the degree of friendliness with which he greets the secretary, the assurance with which he expresses his wish, the calm or nervousness with which he waits, whether he uses his time to read the magazines at his disposal or to look ahead of him in boredom, trepidation or annoyance, whether he is suitable for the vacant post.

The American partiality for mechanical patents has created a large series of machines for judging and assessing human beings. Tape-recording instruments, television equipment, cameras and complicated calculating machines are introduced. The chronograph, invented by the anthropologist, Eliot Chaple, is said to be able to measure the initiative, skill, friendliness and other qualities of the good salesman with ninety-per-cent exactitude.

But the most uncanny of the machines is the polygraph, now employed by at least three hundred American firms and popularly called the lie detector. When it became known that this apparatus had been installed by important government offices of national defense, for use in the selection of their personnel, a storm was raised in the press against such a violation of the rights of personal freedom. This practice is said to have then been abandoned. But the business world was untouched by the wave of protest, and there the polygraph is used more and more.

At first the lie detector was employed only by the police for the purpose of obtaining confessions. Then the private-detective agencies added polygraph departments in order to be able to offer their clients this new service. Banks, insurance companies and similar types of enterprise in which there was danger of embezzlement began to make use of the new apparatus with great success. Department stores and chain stores followed suit. They started the practice of sending their employees every three months for a polygraph test, on the correct assumption that fear of such an examination would eliminate or substantially reduce the small thefts from the stockrooms customary in such businesses. When

the armaments industry was obliged to conceal more and more
of its work, the trial by lie detector was made a prerequisite to
the engagement of any person whose function it would be to deal
with confidential orders of the armed forces.

How precisely the lie detector, which has been constantly bet-
tered since its beginnings, can work I learned for myself when the
polygraph specialists of the Los Angeles police consented to put
me through a test. It was agreed that I should answer a number of
personal questions, sometimes truly, sometimes with a lie. The questions of the examiner were to be so formulated as to be answered
with a *yes* or *no*. I lied about my age, my birthday, my actions
at a certain hour the previous day and the sum of money I had in
my wallet. Although it was only a game, with no emotions of fear
or guilt to assist the discovery, the tester recognized three lies out
of four with certainty and one with near certainty. The most
astonishing feature was its ability to detect not only a lie but a
doubt. I had hesitated in my mind as to whether I had sixteen or
eighteen dollars on me. This hesitation was plainly noted by the
instrument even though I naturally did not alter the expression of
my face.

I had occasion later to accompany a private polygraph specialist
to his work in the personnel division of an aircraft factory near
Los Angeles. He allowed me, after I had been presented as his as-
sistant—a white lie of which the tester was not ashamed—to par-
ticipate in a real truth trial.

It took place in a room without windows which even in the daytime was artificially illuminated with soft indirect lighting, a
semi-twilight intended to remove any irritation and have a relax-
ing effect. There was no sound from without, the temperature
was mild and even and the walls were painted a friendly cream
color.

The girl to be tested sat down in a comfortable leather armchair
with a high back which was turned to the desk. To her were now
deftly attached a number of hooks and buckles. The tester chatted
with her informally meanwhile about general topics.

"Do you still live in the same Motor Court as when you applied for the interview?" he asked sympathetically. "That wouldn't do in the long run. Myself, I shouldn't be able to bear it. Those car noises early in the morning when the overnight guests move on . . ."

"Oh, no," she prattled, very rapidly. "We had such a stroke of luck and found a little place right away with a built-in kitchen corner. Altogether everything has gone so smoothly up to now. When I saw your advertisement in our local paper in Allentown I said to Bill—that's my husband—there's our chance to go west at last. He agreed right away and here we are."

"That's fine," said the tester. "When you come out here quite new you often have trouble finding a place to live."

"Yes," she said, "we were specially lucky."

"Now make yourself quite comfortable," said the examiner; "what's the excitement? there's no need for it."

"The whole thing's a bit unusual. I feel as if I were on the electric chair with that stuff around my arm and on my chest."

"I won't hurt you," the man assured her as he turned the second contact button. "The sling round your right upper arm measures your blood pressure, the rubber coil over the chest your breathing and the two metal disks on the joints of your hands the moisture of the skin. If you find the test disagreeable, you are, of course, free to refuse it."

"If all this is really necessary for getting the job . . ."

"I fear it is necessary. It's for a position of confidence, you know. Just answer my questions truthfully. That's all I ask of you."

Before him on the table lay the questionnaire which the applicant had filled in.

"Your name is Erna Krazinsky?"

"Yes."

"You were born in Troy, New Jersey?"

"Yes."

"Your last post was with Johnson and Johnson?"

"Yes."

"You left the post voluntarily?"

"Yes."

"Or were you dismissed?"

"No . . . I said voluntarily."

"Please answer only *yes* or *no*," he repeated in his kind, imperturbable voice.

"Did you eat meat yesterday evening?"

"Yes."

"Is your father still alive?"

"No."

"Did you come to California ten days ago?"

"Yes."

"You were never before in California?"

"No."

"You went to high school for four years?"

"Yes."

"Are you married?"

"Yes."

"You have children?"

"No."

"You are twenty-six years old?"

"Yes."

"Were you ever divorced?"

"No."

"Good, Mrs. Krazinsky," said the tester, "the torture is over. Was it really so bad?" He loosened the various bindings with which she had been attached to the chair and patted her laughingly on the shoulder. "You've done your bit well," he said kindly.

"May I possibly know the result?" asked the candidate, raising a coquettish eye to him as she smoothed her skirt.

"Sorry," said the interviewer, "the result is naturally confidential. But we'll soon write to you."

When she had passed through the door, he wrote on the upper left-hand side of the questionnaire a large 45.

"That means," he explained to me, "that Mrs. Krazinsky is only 45 per cent truthful. So she hasn't the faintest chance of getting the job. For the posts advertised only candidates 100 per cent honest are considered. Besides, she knew she practically hadn't a chance, else she wouldn't have made that attempt at flirting just before she left. But the polygraph doesn't react to flirting."

The rectangular box standing on the tester's desk had, then, weighed and found wanting. With its buttons, its tension gauge and the paper drum covered with curving signs written on it by automatic pencils, it resembled in many ways the control instruments I had seen on the boards of power houses, steel smelters and atomic factories. There they disclosed the pressure of a boiler, the strength of a current. Here they measured heartbeats, breathing, cold sweat, blood pressure, and it was possible to infer thereby what had taken place in the innermost thoughts of a man.

"Mrs. Krazinsky has lied certainly twice, probably three times," stated the tester. "She did not come to California ten days ago for the first time. That's certain. Every time the conversation touched on the topic the polygraph needles deflected. Here at the very beginning, when we were still chatting about indifferent things, the curves run even. But when I—quite innocently, by the way, and without intending to put a test question—spoke of the housing shortage for newcomers, the apparatus reacted so clearly that I decided to put the question again later on. And this time the deflection was even greater. In between came neutral questions which I knew would be answered truthfully. Hardly anyone lies when you ask him what he's eaten. By such questions I establish the normal level of excitement. Anything that goes beyond it is suspicious."

"Why do you think she lied on that particular point?" I asked.

"Oh, there are a number of possible reasons. Perhaps she only wanted to arouse the interviewer's sympathy by making it seem she had come here all the way from Pennsylvania just for the sake of this job. It may be, too, that she's worked in one or more firms round about Los Angeles and been dismissed from all of them. That seems to be the most likely. Because, look, the question about the last post brings another strong hook on all four measuring curves. And do you see the jump here at the question about whether she's married? The blood-pressure gauge and the skin contact gauge show that something is not in order there. The breathing gauge and the heart curve are unclear. There's something odd about that, too. Probably she lives with someone she isn't married to."

Certainly the use of the lie detector for personnel selection represents the limit of the psychotechnical invasion of personality, and it would be unfair to judge all the accomplishments of industrial psychology by the exaggerations for which it is responsible.

But even the far more innocent and ethically unobjectionable techniques of counseling, the public-opinion polls and the promotion of happy industrial relations, have indirect effects all too reminiscent of similar phenomena in the totalitarian states. Knowing that before and during their employment they are being watched by people in whose hands lie their economic fate, many who wish to keep their jobs speak in a way that does not reflect their true feelings.

Millions of Americans, as soon as they cross the threshold of their place of work, step, partly consciously, partly almost unconsciously, into roles which correspond to what the soul engineers expect of them. They are happy, and "keep smiling" even when they do not feel so inclined. They act as though they were "well balanced" and "perfectly normal" even when they have a tremendous urge to kick over the traces. They strain every fiber to suppress their natural aggressiveness and to be "good companions" with whom everyone easily gets along, even when they would like to break into loud curses at the man at the next desk. And above all, they behave as though they were loyal to the firm through thick and thin, even if they find more to criticize in it than to praise.

This standard mask of the "jolly good fellow," of the "easy going guy," of the "sweet girl," grows onto some of them as a second face. It is no longer a question of the inner conscience, of a true impulse of the soul, but of codes of behavior coming from the outside. To judge how the wind from the heights of the directors' offices will blow, how the potential giver of an order would like the salesman to behave, to guess how a superior pictures the man whom he will promote, this is the most important asset in the battle for a living. In place of rules and regulations imposed by the authorities appears a far stricter self-censorship. Be sure to do nothing striking or unusual, which could be regarded as neurotic, as egotistical, as maladjusted or perhaps even revolutionary.

Thus in the "world without walls" which has increasingly come to be, the type of man on which America's greatness was based is becoming rarer and rarer: the strong, free man guided by his own conscience, constantly searching for something new. Since four out of five Americans today are employees (as against one in five a hundred years ago, a profound alteration in the national character is taking place, a contradiction of the democratic tradition and a cause of concern to every friend of America.

FAIRY-TALE TELLERS OF OUR TIME

New York City, New York

THE FAIRY-TALE TELLERS of our time sit in the market place just as their oriental predecessors did. But this market is a square of some six acres and instead of palm trees, skyscrapers grow in it. It lies on the rocky island of Manhattan between Forty-second and Fifty-ninth Streets and Park and Madison Avenues. There the modern fabulists, the creators of symbols, the weavers of synthetic wonder yarns, have set up their tents, and when they are not addressing their hundred and fifty million listeners, they are busy devising new fairy tales among themselves.

"How about a flying horse?" suggests one of them. "Sticks in the memory. High-grade psychological association. Something quite different for a change."

"Who's interested in flying horses?" another asks dubiously. "It would go right over their heads. They want something nearer home. I propose a stork. Everyone knows what the stork does. They like storks."

"Nonsense," says the first, nettled, "a stork has no class. A common creature. Smells of low income and diapers. But a ruby-red horse spreading its wings. That has breeding. That's something entirely different."

Yes, the modern fairy-tale tellers who disguise themselves as Harun-al-Rashid and think no one will recognize them if they solemnly call themselves advertising consultants do not have an easy life. Their million listeners are blasé. There are simply too many fairy-tale tellers and they deluge their hearers with ever-

201

new stories about living fairies and pots of gold within reach. But the eyes no longer watch, the ears no longer wish to hear. The belief in miracles has been shattered since the new mouthwash did not, as promised, bring a prince to the wallflower, since the honest traveling salesman has noticed that he remains a traveling salesman even though he has been eating Wonder bread, shaving with the magnetic blade, buying the car which carries him as on wings and smoking the cigarette that gives him distinction. What an easy time the storytellers had who spoke only of marvels that could not be bought in the chain stores. Who would think much of Aladdin's lamp if he could really buy it (with a week's guarantee) and try it out? Probably it would be lying unnoticed, like all the other fabulous gadgets forgotten in a corner, long before the thousand-and-one nights were up.

But the fairy-tale tellers do not allow themselves to be discouraged by stirring doubts. They will manage to prick the horny skin of cynicism; they will break through the circle of unbelief; in the end they will penetrate the entrenchments of caution to the citadel of the buyer's soul.

One has simply got to start a little more cunningly and think up surprise tactics; one must spy out the defenses of the disappointed, understand their plan of resistance and outwit it by skillful maneuvers. The psychologists and the founders of public opinion, the market investigators, sociologists, anthropologists and ethnologists, are employed at good salaries by the advertising bureaus to prepare the fresh campaign: science must assist in the fight for clients and must invent new weapons.

But sometimes a simple soul succeeds, without the learned assistance of mass persuasion, in delighting his fellow citizens, who still remain, despite all disillusions, hungry for fairy tales. Once there was a young man from the State of Alabama who set forth to bring wonder to the New Yorkers. There is nothing more difficult than that. Sooner may a stone be kneaded, sooner a thousand-year-old bramble bush blossom, sooner the night turn into day. And yet his daring was crowned with success.

For he presented New York with the large light advertisements, the "spectaculars." He painted on the face of the sky-scrapers light letters six or seven stories high, he let gleaming drops of coffee fall out of gigantic cups, he created rain or snow, he planted in the heart of Manhattan roses higher than church steeples. Clowns and dogs romped as shadows across his light beds of ten thousand lamps, over the heads of the multitude enormous smiling mouths puffed out real smoke rings or shimmering soap bubbles which vanished into nothing, and a dazzling waterfall sparkled above Times Square, a bit of lost nature taken prisoner and brought bound into the free circus of the streets of New York.

And when presently they began to take all these marvels for granted, the young man sent a flamingo to fly across the skies of the city who every now and then let a large dripping orange fall from his beak. No, nobody picked it up, nobody found it afterward. For it hadn't really fallen, it was only a series of neon signs mounted on a small airship.

The young man, whose name is Douglas Leigh, grew rich because he gave the so blasé yet so fairy-tale-hungry New Yorkers a gift of a little bit of dream and fantasy.

As I sat opposite him in his office he said: "What didn't we promise the man in the street during the last war? And what did he get? I at least give the people something: a little color, movement, beauty. I bring light into their lives. Or can you still imagine a New York without 'spectaculars'?"

I tried. I pictured to myself this city without the bright, crazy, unreal never-dull world of Mr. Leigh and the other fairy-tale tellers. There remained little except a gray, furrowed, weather-beaten face: a heap of stones, a torrent of noise, a pointless running hither and thither under a sky out of which no large flamingo drops a shining orange that no one can pick up.

MRS. AVERAGE

Columbus, Ohio

To BE EXACT, there is no Mrs. Average. If she existed she would be worth more to the American advertising industry than the most glamorous film star. She would be assailed daily with hundreds of questions, she would never be left out of sight in all the twenty-four hours of her day, she would get her million-dollar fees with the one condition that she should not receive a penny until after several years. For if she could draw it from the bank she would at once lose her most precious quality, that of being Mrs. Average.

To guess the tastes and requirements of the average customer is the popular never-ending game of the American consumer industry. About fifty thousand market investigators, inquirers into public opinion, results testers, statistical analysts and psychological advisers are exclusively occupied day by day in foretelling, at least approximately, the behavior of the incalculable consumer.

The market researchers, too, belong to the clan of the fairy-tale tellers. Without them no modern advertising bureau could exist. At all events, they would like to end their reports: "And they lived happily ever after. . . ." And since they have not yet found the real Mrs. Average their stories bear boring titles such as "The Increased Birth Rate in New England," "Consumer Jury of 5,500 People in the State of Pennsylvania," or "The Purchasing Habits of 2,632 Customers of a Supermarket in Southern California." According to the behavior of the heroes of this mass epic, the propaganda changes its tone, places the accent on this or on that. Before a new product is baptized its name is read to several thousand average persons. Then they are shown the packaging. Then the slogan under which the new article is to be sold is tried on them, and finally the announcements, the posters, the radio and television programs which are to advertise the new product.

Thus we learn that a hair dye must be advertised as a hair sheen, else the customers whose hair is beginning to turn gray are ashamed to ask for it. An air-line company addresses its comforting advertisements not so much to the largely masculine travelers as to the family who stay at home and are afraid an accident may befall the breadwinner. Fear and shame, bright hopes and secret dreams, every possible movement of the soul in every changing moment of contemporary history must be tracked down, measured, analyzed and put to use to give the advertisement exactly the right effect. Intuition alone must be mistrusted. Nothing but scientific dissection of the mass soul promises results.

No, Mrs. Average, the woman with the most average average-behavior does not exist. But the gnomes and dwarfs of advertising research believe they have found several Mrs. Near-Averages. And the city of Columbus in the State of Ohio seems to be blessed with a particularly large number of these near-standard creatures.

I stopped in Columbus only because I had heard that this town of about half a million inhabitants was the "test tube" of American market research. Apparently the majority of the nation buys what Columbus buys, eats what Columbus eats, likes what Columbus likes and rejects what Columbus rejects.

Hundreds of near-average housewives in Columbus regularly fill in questionnaires for a large market-research firm in Chicago describing in detail what they have bought each month. Hundreds receive thousands of telephone calls or personal visits from market researchers wishing their opinion on the latest wrapping of a "home permanent wave," an egg beater, whipped cream that keeps for a month, or to try out a "commercial," one of those ingenious couplets which, in the course of a few months, will appear several hundred million times in newspapers, on posters and, above all, in the radio programs if . . . yes, if the (nearly) average housewives in (nearly) average Columbus approve.

Mrs. Near-Average in Columbus has even, in return for a few prizes in goods, taken a little mechanical spy into her house. This is the Nielson Corporation's "audiometer" which is built into her radio and spends twenty-four hours a day noting which station and which program she listens to, and for how long she has listened. A bit of perforated paper, which will later be evaluated by office machines on the Nielson premises, is a ballot in the weekly vote that determines which radio and television programs have the greatest appeal. Mrs. Near-Average is not surprised when the Ford Company has the contacts of the psycho-galvanometer (a variety of the lie detector) attached to her pulse and upper arm in order to find out how strongly, in reading the paper, she reacts to the Ford advertisements. She is accustomed to being invited by "Audience Research" to the production of a film not yet publicly released, for the sake of her opinion. Naturally, precise and detailed information is wanted. Therefore she is handed an instrument at the entrance to the cinema on which, by pressing a lever, she will intimate whether she has been very interested, moderately interested or uninterested. This sample of public reaction, neatly registered on a roll inside the instrument, will later be worked up into a report for the purpose of determining which scenes must be deleted from the film because they have failed to interest Mrs. Near-Average.

Mrs. Near-Average has thus become something in the nature of a dictator of taste. Before her the great in the directorial offices and film studios tremble. In the advertising agencies her word is law. Thus, little by little she begins to feel herself a connoisseur. She starts to develop a feeling for quality, the beginning of taste and even a sense of responsibility. And this is the moment that the market researcher must recognize in time. For now Mrs. Near-Average is no longer what she pretends to be. She has lost her innocence, she has acquired qualities which separate her from the mass. So from one day to the next she receives no more questionnaires, no samples, no telephone calls, no visits and no invitations. She has been dethroned.

THE PIED PIPER

Boston, Massachusetts

"YOU MUST EXCUSE Johnnie," said the lady of the house as we sat down to dinner, "he doesn't eat with us in the evenings any longer but picnics in the corral with the other cowboys." She tried to smile and her husband made an effort to sketch a discreet "Hiyooo" in the cowboy style. Then we spooned our soup in silence. The parents had at first been a trifle relieved when their eight-year-old son stopped taking his evening meal with them. At last they could speak freely again at table on any topic they chose, were not interrupted by endless questions, did not have to exhort Junior to eat nicely. But now they had begun to miss him.

"Do excuse me," said the lady of the house again, "I must just see whether Johnnie is drinking his milk." With that she vanished into the next room. As she opened the door the thud of hoof-beats came in to us for a moment, and the shrill mechanical tones of a musical accompaniment. "There was nothing else to do," explained the host; "the child was simply not to be held once the 'Hoppy Show' had begun. Slid about on his chair, stuffed down the last mouthfuls in a hurry, or else left half his plate untouched, anything to get back quickly to his television set. Now we serve his meal in there on the folding table. He eats and watches. Imagines with all his soul he is a regular cowboy and greets me when I come with his silver revolver drawn and an affectionate 'Hands up.' "

Johnnie's case is typical of what happened to innumerable American families when the television set entered their lives. It seemed as though the Pied Piper, once followed by the children of Hamelin on the Weser, had been resurrected in the United States. Almost without exception the children of America have followed the call of this newcomer. While grownups, as soon as the charm of novelty has worn off, find a pace for the TV set among other minor interests and amusements, the boys and girls are insatiable. Children between the ages of three and thirteen spend many hours daily before the little magic screen that offers them stories without cease, adventures, jokes, thrilling detective yarns, and in between salvos of advertising slogans.

The television set gratifies the children's natural hunger for adventure far more thoroughly than the picture book has ever been able to do. It is a tireless story teller which always has time. Even three- or four-year-olds are able to perform the simple act of snapping on the current. No longer do they need to acquire reality painstakingly, bit by bit: it is already there, in the middle of the parental living room.

Like most of what will later be offered for sale to these young Americans, whether in the form of food, music, or the theater, it is selected, prepared and put up in potted form by others. The perfect consumer, who is dependent on the creativeness and taste of an ever-decreasing number of producers, is formed at an early age, before experiences of his own have been able to affect his character, or his own fantasies to unfold in a normal way.

"The children no longer do their homework," complain the teachers. "It's impossible to get Junior to go to sleep," say the mothers. And the fathers are horrified at the language of their off-spring. "The devil take it," raged an eight-year-old, as reported by the television critic of *The New York Times*. "If I have to go along to see Grandpa someone will bear the consequences." Thereupon he ran the water tap and mixed a deadly poisonous drink as he had seen done in the television serial *Suspense*. A small girl, passing a tavern with her father, chirped what she had learned from the TV advertisements: "Ask for Ballantine's beer."

When I heard these stories for the first time I laughed, as one does at the sayings of children. Only when I saw children in a

West Hollywood street singing advertising couplets set to music in place of the old nursery songs, and when a few weeks later in a gigantic new Van Nuys supermarket I heard a small boy in a black cowboy suit urge his mother: "Please, Mummy, buy only 'Barbara Ann' bread. Hoppy says it makes him strong," did I begin to understand the game: through television the advertising bureaus had turned millions of little boys and girls into voluntary agents. The American citizen, hardened against propaganda, may ignore certain enticements. But when a child's voice pleads, who—particularly in America—can resist?

The discovery of the child market is not of recent date. The promoters of the breakfast foods sold in variegated cartons built up their business on the children's good will. The firm which accompanied its packages with the prettiest prizes (or which offered them on receipt of the carton lid) could count on the largest youthful clientele. Thus "Wheaties," shortly after the launching of the first atomic bomb, outstripped all its rivals by promising its young customers an "atom ring with radioactive substance."

But these things were a mere prelude to the greatest spectacle of child mass hysteria since the distant days of the Children's Crusade. It dated from the rise of an old cowboy actor, Bill Boyd, in the television role of the virtuous Hopalong Cassidy, to become the idol of the youth of an entire nation. In reality Hoppy was neither so virtuous nor so brave as he was represented. He had long led a notoriously wild life and hated nothing so much as locomotion on the back of a horse. But that was of no importance: the fairy-tale tellers had found in him a mythical hero of stature and harnessed him to their various advertising chariots in a way they had never before used a living person.

Not only were a million cowboy suits (at $20 to $45) sold in a few months, but also nearly as many pistols (50 cents to $5.50), spurs ($2 to $4), knives (60 cents to $7), and riding books ($4 to $9). And as the Hoppy enthusiasm continued to grow, other producers of the most varied objects, by no means necessarily for the use of the young, were seized with Hoppy madness. In return for five per cent of the selling price, Hopalong Cassidy was prepared to let himself be made patron of savings banks, bakery firms, necktie designers, watchmakers, chocolate factories and brands of soap. About five hundred various Hoppy products appeared on the market and were purchased by the parents of twenty-five million children.

That went on until the Hoppy symbol, through a carefully planned and cleverly carried out counterattack by a group of advertising people, gradually lost ground. A radio program with the Space Cadet Tom Corbett as its hero, a sort of interplanetary cowboy who disposed of his opponent with the death-ray pistol, began its triumphal journey on television.

I saw the downfall of Hoppy and the rise of his rival foreshadowed on the evening I had to dine with my Boston hosts without the presence of Johnnie. To his father's astonishment the hostess returned from the living room, from which emerged the sound of Hoppy's gallop, not alone as we had expected, but accompanied by her offspring, a pale little boy who remarked by way of explanation: "That guy is beginning to bore me."

A month later his father had bought him a space suit ($24.50), an antidote against cosmic rays (sweets at 60 cents) and a pair of antigravity shoes ($7.20). And when he came home his son received him with a loud "Hands pu"—which is not much more difficult to pronounce than "Hands up" and is well known to mean the same in the language of Mars—as he pointed the ray gun ($3.98) at him. Papa obeyed this order without delay, and before the raised arms had time to descend his Johnnie had already vanished to consume his supper aboard a space rocket.

BEAUTY ON THE MARKET

Hollywood, California

WHERE DO ALL the pretty girls disappear to, who come daily from all over America hoping for a film job in Hollywood? Sometimes you see one of them on Hollywood Boulevard looking at a shop-window display or at the posters outside a movie. Or one of these beauties is behind the cash desk at Schwab's, the little drugstore at the corner of Sunset Boulevard and Laurel Canyon, where film people buy their cigarettes, gulp a cup of coffee and throw a glance at the almighty newspaper of their profession, the *Hollywood Reporter*. A few days later she has disappeared. Did someone, while he was waiting for his change, discover her? Or has she fallen into the trap of a fast talker who made her dazzling promises?

"Beauty alone is no longer a draw," say the film people. "Our actresses must have some understanding of their profession. A sweet face, a well-proportioned body, are not enough." That may be generally true, but now and then a young thing with a dreamy eye, a provocative figure and an iron will, who shrinks from nothing, does succeed in putting herself across. At most this is accomplished by one girl in a thousand. She gets a starlet contract, is instructed for a couple of months at the expense of a film company and if she then turns out to be gifted . . . But only one out of two dozen starlets finally gets a real contract and real —even if at first small—roles. The others soon drop out of the running. They marry a shopkeeper from Beverly Hills (if they are lucky), become the friend of a rich man, emerge (if they are

213

unlucky) as the latest "telephone number" passed on from man
to man. But only very few beauties sink melodramatically stage
by stage. Most of them become honest, industrious wage earners
who make their five to six hundred dollars a month by selling
their most charming smile, their most entrancing gestures, their
best-performed ecstasy for fifteen to twenty-five dollars an hour.
Oh, there is nothing dishonorable about it: they are not prosti-
tuting themselves. They have merely become models, with the
task of seducing the toiling male to buy a can of beer, an automobile and a thousand other objects.

For no symbol draws in America like the glamour girl. When
nothing else enters the heads of the fairy-tale tellers, one of them
is sure to propose, "How about a little cheesecake?" which could
be translated to mean "spice." With this the dullest dishes can
be made less insipid. Who would pay the slightest attention to
an advertisement for glue if the eye were not arrested by
the sweet smile of a dark-haired model with light-blue eyes? How
better can one dramatize the presentation of potato chips than
by the choice of a Potato Chips Queen who lends her radiant
beauty to the prosaic surplus of a too-large potato crop? Like god-
desses they come down to the ordinary mortal and offer him out
of their cornucopias the sum total of the products of civilization:
from aspirin to zonite, from construction machines as high as
houses to tiny tablets against bad breath. "Sex is our Number
One sales gun," the advertising people admit. Even specialists
washed in all the waters of social psychology and mass analysis
have not yet been able to think out anything more efficacious
than well-formed feminine legs or a bosom which merely pretends to hide itself from view.

Harmless as this game of enticement for purposes of business
appears at first glance to be, it is in reality not so. For it turns
Prometheus into Tantalus. Allurement in four-colored printing,
promises on glazed paper, "perhaps" intimated from posters
magnified a hundredfold, bring into the life of the American man
an undertone of nervous tension which, in a country ruled at
least ostensibly by Puritan morals, has more difficulty in find-

ing relief than anywhere in Europe. How far this pin-up eroti-
cism, prolonged to saturation point, has already stimulated a mass
neurosis is difficult to estimate, but a number of serious psychi-
atrists regard the two-dimensional glamour girl, the pictured
beauty, the ubiquitous compensation for reality, as the most dangerous will-o'-the-wisp now being pursued by Americans. Naturally, in the world of the model there is also a stepladder of prestige. At the top stand the cover girls and fashion models, highly
paid by the photographers and able to earn as much in a year as
the third vice president of a bank or a secretary of state ($15,000
to $25,000). They must, to be sure, lead a very strenuous shadow
existence. Bound by far stricter dietary rules than any film
star, they often half-starve themselves to death, drive away their
appetites with benzedrine and in so doing borrow from their
small reservoirs that irreplaceable store of energy which permits
them to endure eight photographic appointments daily under the
hottest artificial light. Of these top models there are not over two
hundred in New York and Hollywood together.

Next comes the middle class of beauty, the multitude of pretty
girls who so strikingly resemble each other as to make it un-
noticeable when one member of the circle of two or three hundred drops out on account of age, marriage, or "silly affairs" and
another appears on the scene. In the make-believe life they lead
in magazines, on posters and on television, they are the brides
who got their man because they always washed with a particular
soap or greased their faces with a certain cream. They are the
happy mothers who give their children only chocolate with vita-
min supplement, look at the new icebox with eyes of love, have
solved all family problems by the purchase of a washing machine and, with a few drops of Tabu perfume, irresistibly lure
the male animal onto their trail.

In actual life these pretty, industrious girls live in the side
streets of Hollywood, where they have rented an average
furnished "bachelor room," or in Forest Hills, New York, in a
small apartment which they share with another model. Their
great hope is that one of the boy friends who take them out will

one day, by an offer of marriage, bring them nearer the world they mime daily, of comfortable family happiness. Since modeling of this sort is in no way regarded as disreputable, many pretty girls end by successfully closing their private advertising campaign with a sale.

The models for lingerie, bathing suits and personal hygiene are less respected than these, but better paid and better regarded than the beauties who pose for piquant calendar pictures, "cheesecake photos," and at yearly businessmen's conventions leap, rather sketchily clad, out of large dummy cakes set in the middle of the festive board.

And then . . . then come the models whom we saw on Santa Monica Boulevard in Hollywood, on the first floor, over a poultry-dealer's shop. The notice in the Los Angeles *Mirror* stated, "Undraped models will pose for serious amateur photographers." For three dollars' admission, which included the rent of the camera and a roll of film, we were allowed to enter a low, stuffy photographic studio in which about a dozen men were already assembled. Eyes, human and photographic, were glassily fixed upon an exquisitely pretty naked girl with long raven-black hair, who sat motionless on a bit of imitation beach under harsh floodlights, pressing to herself an enormous ball.

Not a word was spoken, no sound heard except now and then the click of a camera. The manager, a lanky man with his glasses askew, encouraged the men who seemed dumb with embarrassment: "Just tell her what position you want. . . ."

Not a sound. Then finally from a sturdy fellow: "Please, Miss. Would you lie down on top of the ball? . . . Yes . . . like that —with the face and hair downward." She obeyed silently, snatched a small towel with which she wanted quickly to hide what had been protected up to now by the ball. In the split second of this change she was quite uncovered, and the cameras clicked like a battery of guns.

"What exposure did you use?" two men asked each other excitedly. "I only photograph details," claimed another, pressing closer to the model. "Can we rearrange the lights?" somebody inquired. He went very near to the beauty lying on the ball, began to shift the floodlight, and in doing so bent down over her. She looked at him open-eyed, without changing her expression. Like a blind woman. "Sit up a little more," cried a more heated voice. She raised herself a trifle, the cameras shot again. Then the lights were turned off for a moment and the beauty vanished without a word into her dressing room, while another undraped model, a little redhead with impudent eyes, stood among the pack of hounds, wrapped in a fish net. They looked spellbound into the view finders, feverishly adjusted the aperture and nervously screwed on supplementary lenses with trembling fingers. "I can't afford a body release," said someone near me.

"Now, boys, what'll it be?" asked the beauty defiantly.

PART SIX

Grasping at the Future

DISCOVERIES TO ORDER

Wilmington, Delaware

AT LUNCH in the employees' restaurant of the largest American chemical firm, Du Pont, I was introduced in these words to a group sitting at the next table: "Meet the Seventies!" Since none of the gentlemen appeared to be over fifty, I weighed for a moment the possibility that I was being shown the objects of an experiment in rejuvenation. The real explanation turned out to be simpler but still highly unusual.

The gentlemen were members of a subdivision of the Development Department which is occupied with devising products for use in the seventies of our century: textile fibers, building materials, metals, photographic processes, fertilizers, traction and explosive fuel for the coming generation.

Half an hour later I was conducted by one of these researchers across the threshold of the next century. We needed no sort of time machine but traveled in a twelve-year-old Buick from the administrative building in Wilmington to a neighboring peninsula surrounded by river and woods, where thirty barracklike yellow brick buildings stood. This is the Experimental Station, built on the grounds of a former golf club. In one of its laboratories I saw written on a door: A.D. 2000.

The date was no joke, I was told by the serious young man who was guiding me. They were trying here to make "educated guesses," through estimates founded on fact, regarding the probable activities of the firm at the beginning of the third millennium. One could, for example, figure out fairly accurately

221

from existing experience how long the completion of certain series of experiments would still require. A careful observation of trends in technical science and economy made it possible to predict with a certain degree of probability which products would be demanded of a chemical concern in the next decade.

He showed me tables with chains of chemical formulas that resembled family trees. But instead of going back into the past they reached out into the future, pointed the way in symbols to still nonexistent productions. There one saw how, out of new compounds, creations were to come into being which, even though themselves still unborn, were again uniting themselves to produce a third generation. Projected into the future was a whole family of children, grandchildren, great- and great-great-grandchildren of fancy, among which at the end was the only, the long-sought one, which made the entire effort valid: the greatly desired "wonder product."

"Here," said the chemist, pointing to one of the plans, "is the new lubricating oil that won't freeze. It is not yet ready, but we'll be able to produce it in 1965 at latest. That, over there, is the fiber out of which we'll weave shirts for hot climates; this, here, is a new building material that can be made to emit light and makes all lamps unnecessary, and there—hardly, by our reckoning, to be brought onto the market before the year 2010—is the dream of mankind: synthetic nourishment, arrived at by imitation of the processes of nature."

He said all this without for a moment seeming a visionary or a braggart. He was as sure of the future as the self-righteous are of the Kingdom of Heaven. Although he was employed by a firm which had begun with the production of gunpowder, expanded during the First World War by the manufacture of high explosives, had built the Plutonium Works at Hanford in the Second World War and was now, on commission from the government, equipping the first hydrogen-bomb factory, on the Savannah River, the Du Pont researcher apparently did not include the possibility of a catastrophic war in his calculations. He was on terms of intimate familiarity with tomorrow and the day after. If that which was to come held terrors for him, he gave no sign of it.

There has always been speculation about the future, particularly in the Western world, but it has probably never been so concrete as in the present-day United States. Here the future is no longer left to religious visionaries or philosophical utopians, but is delivered up to a group of specialized scientists who, with the help of acceleration curves, graphs of the future, repetition cycles, current plans and tables of probability, predict, with as much precision as possible, the things which are to come.

The Americans do not care, as do thinkers in other countries, to philosophize about the future but rather to do something about it: to conquer it and, in so far as is humanly possible, control its direction and marching steps. With the possible exception of Soviet Russia and her satellites there is no country on earth in which so much planning is being done as in the United States.

The concern of economy with the future has proved successful because banks and industrial firms are sometimes in a position to "make the future." This is true particularly in one connection: the conscious furtherance or curbing of new technical inventions.

New inventions since the beginning of the present century have repeatedly struck the working world with the impact of forces of nature. The automobile, electricity, the invention of mass production, shook the community and drove it to a hasty adaptation often fraught with hardship. To avoid the repetition of such revolutions, to allow the new to break through by slow degrees, is a principal objective in American planning.

The sociologist S. C. Gilfillan has done pioneer work in this connection. He has shown that each invention needs about thirty-five to fifty years for full development. A man able to discover the possibilities of an invention at its birth can foresee a great number of inventive possibilities for the future. Thus, for example, the electro-engineer Charles P. Steinmetz was able in 1915 to predict a large series of inventions which would eventually be made in his field. In fact, 76 per cent of these prophecies were confirmed (in part after his death), 24 per cent were partially correct and not one entirely erroneous.

Building on a basis of the predictability of inventions, large American enterprises such as General Electric have established "schools for inventors" for gifted members of the rising generation, in which invention is taught as the art of the combination of two knowns for the creation of an unknown third.

Nowhere in America has the effort toward systematic recognition and purposeful conquest of the future been carried on with so much energy and success as in the chemical industry. This profession has understood how to foretell coming demands by careful analysis of future developments and, on the other hand, by means of its own marvels, has itself actively influenced the future.

The result—favored by the long absence of the German chemical industry in the contest for world markets—is impressive: the chemical industry, in the thirteen years between 1937 and 1950, wrested first place from the automobile industry. The key word for this rise was "research"—active, purposeful exploration directed at the future.

The firm of Du Pont has again conquered and held the highest place within the chemical industry by a sort of mass attack on the secrets of nature. Two thousand scientists are at work in the thirty-three Du Pont laboratories. They are endowed with a yearly budget of thirty to thirty-five million dollars, turn out an average of one new patent, ready for marketing, on each of the 365 days of the year and have constantly about a thousand projects in hand, one in every ten of which, approximately, leads to positive results.

Should a highly gifted and strong-willed individual fall into this strictly regulated mass formation, friction and disappointment must inevitably result. An example is Wallace Hume Carothers who, in 1927, at the age of thirty-one, was taken out of his laboratory at Harvard University by one of Du Pont's talent scouts and brought to Wilmington. Here he succeeded in February, 1935, as a result of his theoretical research, in developing the basic fiber for a synthetic thread able to resist temperatures of 500 degrees Fahrenheit. It was first called "Polyamid 66" and was later baptized "Nylon."

Carothers was of the opinion that once he had found the solution in principle he could discover additional, far more durable fibers, and in fact later demonstrated this. But the firm of Du Pont did not wish to wait for a further improvement but to appear on the market as quickly as possible in order to reap the full benefit of their patent, which ran for only seventeen years. Carothers' far superior fiber, labeled with the laboratory name of "5-10," was not put into production, despite his pleas. In January 1940, five years after the discovery, Du Pont brought out nylon in quantity. But Carothers did not live to see the opening of the first nylon factory. In 1937, ten years after his resignation from Harvard, he committed suicide.

THE ELECTRONIC ORACLE

Washington, D.C.

IT WAS one of those extraordinary days when Washington, otherwise as composed and restrained as a fashionable suburb, vibrated with political unrest. "A famous war hero brusquely dismissed," announced the ticker tapes. The excitement over this decision pierced through the green isolation belt of the parks, ran the straight length of the streets, kindled innumerable debates and was reflected back onto the cool, tree-shaded marble façades of the government buildings.

In the garden of the government testing office, the National Bureau of Standards, politics are seldom discussed. Here they concern themselves with the inflammability of textiles; debate the advantages and disadvantages of new artificial threads; explore the properties of chemicals; send out impulses to the moon, in the hope of obtaining an echo from it. But on this day, excitement over the inaccurate and scarcely measurable phenomenon of politics seemed to have seized even the professional investigators of the N.B.S.

As we walked through the large park in which the many laboratory buildings, the demonstrating and testing stations lie embedded, the air was heavy, saturated with that moist indolence which brings Washington climatically into the orbit of the South. My companion had made the blossoming cherry tree, presented half a century ago to the Americans by the Japanese, an occasion for airing his views on the foreign policies of the United States. But before he had finished his exposition we found ourselves

227

standing in front of two low buildings of the provisional type
known in the capital as "W.W.II (World War II) style."

"Do you know the decision to call off the General was fundamentally taken in these two sheds?" my guide asked me.

I wanted to protest that, as everyone knew, the decision to fire
the war hero had been taken by the much-praised and much-
cursed "man in the White House." But my companion had already vanished into the doorway of one of the two frail houses
over whose entrance could be read: "National Bureau of Standards Eastern Automatic Computer" (SEAC). I knew, of course,
that in these unpretentious buildings one of the newest electronic
brains was housed. I had come in order to see the fabulous creation close at hand. But with the best will in the world I was unable
to grasp any possible connection between this highly developed
laboratory instrument and the political *affaire célèbre* of the day.

My friend brought me into a small room where there was no
one but ourselves and a slim young man with a rather bored expression, feeling around on a keyboard of black buttons and
levers. The instrument reminded me strongly of one of those con-
soles with many registers used by organists. The organist here
also read his notes from a sheet. Over his shoulder I could see
many dots and dashes, arranged in varied patterns, which apparently were his score.

My companion, not to disturb the other man, made a mute
gesture in the direction of two round television screens embedded
in the middle of the console: there one saw constantly changing
figures and arabesques written by a whitish-blue point of light on
a green latticed grid and then immediately effaced. They must
have been signs from within the machine, which was hidden behind a partition—reports on the nature of its work, its opinion,
the progress of its complicated thinking operations.

When the operator allowed his fingers a moment's rest, my
companion introduced me. Then he said: "What are you working on today, Ed?"

The other looked up, bored. "Nothing special. Still the old
175 to 175 grid. At four, Francis wants a flood problem run

through. And then there's an express order from the Air Force boys. The usual stuff: whirlwind calculations, resistance tests. But that has nothing to do with me. I'll be finished in half an hour and go. By the way, what do you say about the General? Incredible, eh? But in my opinion . . ." He interrupted himself; for a blinking orange light had appeared on the console and at the same time we heard a rattle as of the fall of type in a composing machine. Little red flares leaped up between the black keys of the control console and on the lower of the two picture screens the whitish-blue point suddenly plunged like a comet, leaving behind it a strong trail of light.

"For the third time," said Ed, resignedly, "for the third time in one day it acts like this." He turned to the wall which separated his piano from the machine and read a little lecture to the curious electronic being behind it: "You neurotic fool. Now I've got to sweat here another two hours on your account and begin all over again from the beginning."

I felt slightly ill at ease, like a guest who is the unwilling witness of a family quarrel.

"SEAC is still going through a few teething troubles," said my guide apologetically; "it's always possible to have a short circuit somewhere, or a few valves may stick, or the emulsion of the sound strip on which the problem is noted shows a microscopic flaw. SEAC is not perfect. It has been living here with us for a year and we know most of its bad habits by now. For instance, it's slow at waking up in the morning, it's extraordinarily sensitive and it at once has a nervous reaction if one gives it too difficult a problem. But these little faults are nothing when you set them against SEAC's accomplishments. Do you know what we call it? 'The Oracle of Washington.' And this hut? 'The Little White House.' "

"Oracle? Then you meant it seriously about the General's dismissal?"

"You mean that SEAC spoke the deciding word? Quite seriously. Things were like this, you see: the General stood for a strategy which would have led our country onto the brink or even into the middle of a world war. Here in Washington there were many adherents of the strong policy. The President might perhaps have had to bow before them in the end if SEAC had not delivered an objective judgment against which there was no reasonable argument. We ran calculations on the thinking machine for several days which we formerly would not have attempted to do at all because it would have taken years. We had to work out how American economy in all its sectors would react to a sudden entry into war at this moment. SEAC gave the answer in clear, unambiguous numbers: even the intensification of aggressive action demanded by the General would cause a considerable shock to our economic system; an outbreak of war at this moment would be premature and might easily be unfavorable to us. Every proposal advanced, every strategic variant was figured out by SEAC down to its final consequence. And these computations were the strongest trump in the President's hand when he decided against the General and his policy."

At the time, I was inclined to consider the foregoing account as an exaggeration. Every specialist tends to overvalue his own significance in the joint undertaking. In a period which drives the individual back into the role of a little wheel among a million little wheels a person is apt to ascribe to himself the role of the decisive little wheel, on whose right functioning the fate of the whole machinery hangs. This feeling of the importance of his personal function is to many a man a substitute for his lost freedom.

But I must now apologize to the man who first enlightened me on the part played by electronic brains in bringing about important political decisions in the United States. He claimed too little rather than too much. The more I pursued these matters in the months that followed, the more I realized with astonishment that the *machine à gouverner* dreamed of by Utopians in past centuries had become a reality.

"To govern is to foresee." Foresight is based not only on intuition but also on the most comprehensive knowledge of the evidence. Among the Washington prophets who made astounding forecasts in the service of the government with the help of abundant statistical materials and electronic brains two American citizens of Russian origin have earned the greatest fame. One of them is Louis Bean, who in 1948 was the only forecaster to prophesy the results of the presidential and congressional elections with a fair degree of accuracy. He worked mainly for the Department of Agriculture, on whose orders he forecast the result of harvests, market conditions for agricultural produce, future inundations and large social movements such as the flight from the land.

Whereas Bean relies at least partly on his intuition, the other great government prophet, Professor Wassily Leontief, is interested exclusively in "objective number content." One of his most important political prophecies was made at the order of the President when the question arose in 1950 whether America, in view of events in Korea, should mobilize completely or only in part. His decision was for partial mobilization.

Professor Leontief had made the goal of his lifework the study of the interrelation of the various branches of American production. His statistical grid groups forty-two principal branches of production and forty-two of consumption in such a way that the relationship of sellers and buyers may be seen in exact percentages; in this way the claim of every branch of economy through every new demand, from a simple increase in air armament to a total mobilization, can be exactly calculated in advance. To arrive at these proportional figures millions of equations had to be worked out beforehand with the help of SEAC.

A first attempt, made by Leontief's methods with the use of the electronic brain shortly after the close of the Second World War, had convinced the government of his exactitude. When the steel industry was expecting a diminution in the demand for steel for the year 1947, Leontief came to a different conclusion: he calculated that America's blast furnaces at that moment would be producing too little steel, and he was proved right. The figure for steel requirements computed by him was correct to within a few hundred tons.

Since then there has been a disposition in Washington to give full credit to scientific forecasting. More, and more exact, statistics were procured from Leontief by various departments, thus making it possible for him to construct a far more detailed grid of 175 production branches and as many consumer groups, so that the forecasts are now becoming increasingly precise. Leontief's calculations are used in the distribution of raw materials to various branches of industry for armament or consumption purposes. The thinking machine of the National Bureau of Standards establishes the quotas to be distributed. The electronic brain has thus become a most important instrument in the economy of planning.

In what measure the electronic brains have participated, since the end of the last war, in decisions relating to foreign and defense policies is veiled in secrecy. It is claimed that the rivalry between the Army, Navy and Air Force, each of which wanted as large as possible a part of the armaments budget for itself, was finally settled by the thinking machine.

In Washington problems of world politics are often expressed in the language of poker, boxing or football. That the comparisons should be chosen particularly from the realm of sport is not without significance. The historical period is conceived of as being determined round by round, by human exertion and intelligence rather than by factors relating to God or to history.

If one wishes to predict the intentions of the rival on the other side of the gaming table, the sports arena or the football field, the straightforward methods of speculation described above will prove inadequate. For they can only produce useful results if the scientific prophet has an abundance of data at his disposal. But in the case of a game, a match, a political fray, this is not to be expected. The opponent keeps his cards secret to the best of his ability, he will do all he can to veil his tactics. In order, therefore, to forecast his behavior, other methods will have to be tried.

Science has for some time been attempting to analyze games of chance according to possible laws and believes it has found certain mathematical rules which may be formulated. The object of a "system" is to enable the player to choose tactics which are promising, even if not infallible. It is therefore not surprising that a "Theory of Games," the work of an eminent mathematician and a Princeton economist, which appeared in 1944, attracted wide interest in Washington.

The scientific rules of bluffing, leading, the weighing of losses and gains, here developed in the manner of poker, with two or at most three players, have been made the foundation of a number of strictly specialized studies of high political significance. Special sections of the General Staff ("Advanced Study Group") and of the Department of State ("Long-Planning Staff") adapt these deadly serious "games" to every new situation. They translate diplomatic notes, armies, armament industries, new weapons, psychological offensives and counteroffensives into the abstract language of poker strategy and have all possible tactical combinations played over to them by electronic brains in order to choose the best solution for their own country and translate the battle for power back into concrete terms.

For the classic example of an unprofitable strategy which might have been avoided by poker mathematics and the thinking machine, the priests of the electronic oracle point to Hitler. Had he not trusted his intuitions, they claim, but used the sum of the efforts he expended on the building of rockets to keeping the mastery of the European air by means of a strong air force, his chances of victory would have been decidedly better.

When I stood opposite the SEAC and heard for the first time the political role played by this thinking machine, I found the idea incredible. Several months later, at Santa Monica on the opposite side of the United States, I visited the RAND Corporation, an institute founded and supported by the Air Force. By now it no longer surprised me to learn that nearly three hundred scientists of the most varied faculties are tracing "pictures of the future" here, to guide the State along its way into the next decade, and even into the next millennium.

H. G. Wells once prophesied such a rule of scientists. The

"gathering of great minds," which meets daily in a suburban street in California, comes closer to this conception than any similar institution. Eight aerodynamic specialists are here, twenty-two national economists, fifty-one mathematicians, two psychologists, four sociologists, forty specialists in the operation of computers and eighty-seven engineers. There are one astronomer, three pure logicians and eight statisticians, and to all of these Washington has said: "Tell us how to act."

The RAND Corporation was originally formed to deal with two large and divergent problems: firstly, the "Strategic Bombing Project" was to consider the intercontinental actions of the American Air Force in case of war, and secondly the "Air Defense of U.S. Project" was to study the possibilities and requirements of a plan of defense.

Soon, however, the scientists were carried beyond their purely military tasks. For the boundaries between strategy and politics fade away in this age of revived power politics. The question, for example, of counterattacks of enemy territory caused the emergence of problems of a social-psychological nature. (Such as: Would such attacks demoralize the civilian population or goad it to stronger resistance?) It became necessary to consider questions of psychological warfare and of the form of society of the probable opponent. Works on the nature of mass movements, the role of the political elite, the rise and fall of states, were discussed.

In the rooms of the shabby old factory building, transformed into offices, imaginary wars were waged, imaginary victories celebrated and imaginary states created in consultation with the best human and artificial brains. Here the future is regarded as an unending chain of political, economic and martial conflicts. It is a melancholy symptom of the times that these branches of science, when they work together for the first time on the theory and practice of administrative problems, should do so under the aegis of destruction.

If one speaks of this to the scholars at the RAND Corporation, they defend themselves by pointing out that science, with rare exceptions, has always been most strongly furthered by the interest of the war lords: peaceful research, as it was carried on for a time, had been the exception, not the rule. Whereupon they return to their war games, which they conduct partly on paper, partly on the electronic brain.

A participant in one of these maneuvers, which are not open to the public, describes it as follows:

"A war between the blue and the red fighting forces was yesterday put through in the air-war simulator. This electronic brain, which works twenty-four hours a day on problems of the RAND Corporation, is at the Wright-Patterson Air Force Base. The various circuits of the computer can be adjusted to represent the entire war strength of the fighting nations with all their inhabited towns, factories, fuel supplies, oil lines, bomber camps and air squadrons.

"The game is played in quick-motion tempo: a day corresponds to ten seconds. Each side receives detailed information about its own possibilities and provisions but no more military reports on the dispositions of the enemy than it would in a real war.

"Every tactical or strategical move is simulated by means of the corresponding electronic switch. The calculating machine can then reckon out mathematically how much the enemy has been damaged.

"As the switches click in the silent room the adversaries' countries are transformed into simulated ruins. Finally the hand on the dial plate of the one party sinks to zero. That means that its cities have been destroyed by explosions, its people exhausted, paralyzed, presumably poisoned by radioactivity, and its entire Air Force lost. The game is up."

The oracle has spoken.

THE RETURN OF THE THINKER

Princeton, New Jersey

SHORTLY BEFORE eleven in the morning the attendant at the Institute for Advanced Studies takes another look to make sure that some fresh pieces of chalk are lying before the blackboard in Room 15.

"The Professor is the most unassuming man you can imagine," he tells me, "but if there aren't any pointed chalks on hand he gets annoyed."

I am allowed a brief glance at the monastically simple room: a table, a chair, an empty bookshelf—that is all. The view from the high window, over a wide expanse of lawn, is cut off in the distance by a clump of large trees, from between whose bare branches a few pretty white houses are visible.

How quiet and peaceful it is here. When, nearly five years ago, a professor invited me for the first time to a lecture at this institute, I was in no position to realize what an exception, what an oasis of meditation, these houses surrounded by greenery, with their studies, libraries and residential rooms, represent in contemporary America. Between times I have seen much of the country. Enough to cause doubt and apprehension. I am afraid for America: afraid of its losing the best of itself, the esteem for freedom and humanity, in the struggle for nearly godlike omnipotence.

There is nobody about except for a small black speck, which appears at the far end of the path and moves slowly in the direction of the main building. Directly in front of the window two men are now walking up and down in lively conversation. They stop in the middle of the path because the talk seems to have reached a particularly difficult or interesting point. The black speck has now come nearer and is recognizable: an old man in a winter overcoat. His thick white hair looks out from under a Persian-lamb cap. He walks slowly, living entirely in a dream full of beautiful equations if one can judge by his absent-minded smile, as he fumbles his way up the few low steps to the entrance. We must be quick to leave his hermitage: Albert Einstein has arrived for his daily three-hour meditation. The clock on the villagelike tower over the middle of the institute building is striking eleven.

The two out there on the carpet of grass did not look up from their dialogue as the great man passed them by. This was not out of disregard but for the contrary reason. Here alone the author of the theory of relativity is not, as elsewhere, an object of gaping curiosity.

The Institute for Advanced Studies in Princeton is one of the most unusual scientific foundations in America. It possesses no laboratories with costly and complicated machines, but offers instead something that may be more important to real progress: time and space for undisturbed meditation. No instruction or diploma is provided here. There is nothing that serves a concrete purpose. Nobody is supervised or tested. All may come and go as they please. A man will perhaps work in his small room day and night for a week on end, or he may give no sign of himself for a long period. Nobody's work is prescribed, and the result of labor belongs to the person who has performed it. The reckoning he owes is to himself and his conscience.

The American pedagogue, Doctor Abraham Flexner, is the spiritual father and founder of the institute. During the optimistic twenties, when the prevailing opinion in America held that all was for the best, he perceived behind the loud demonstrations a flight—camouflaged as an attack—from awakening doubts, and an inner incapacity of man to keep pace with material progress.

At first Flexner's idea of creating a place for contemplation found little approbation among those whom he approached for contributions. But just when money for philanthropic purposes had become scarcer than ever before, after the crisis of 1929, the pedagogue found wealthy patrons in the department-store owner, Louis Bamberger, and his sister Mrs. Fuld. Their foundation of five millions was an act of faith. They wished to say by this gesture that America's rise could be only temporarily checked through the economic crisis, but that it was important to understand the warning sign of the depression and, instead of clinging to a boundless optimism, call back to mind the great guiding spiritual principles.

The root of the new institute was the School of Mathematics, but it was soon realized that in a time of great political upheavals a need existed for genuine historical knowledge which might well be stimulated by contact with the sober discipline of pure reason. So a School of Historical Studies was added whose members make dispassionate investigations, ranging from archaeology to contemporary history, of how man has lived and compounded with his destiny.

The mathematical and theoretical physicists in Princeton have shown a keen interest in these historical studies. Some of them had had painful personal experience of history in Europe and had been brusquely startled out of their conception of the self-evidence of a civilized order. From their own experience and historical absorption they now began to see objective science as not entirely separable from ethics nor free from responsibility. So the natural scientists of the institute have turned toward the humanities.

The new head of the institute, chosen after the last war, symbolizes this significant return. Robert Oppenheimer had directed the construction of the first atomic bomb during the Second World War. After the war he went to Princeton "to work for the preservation of the good things for which man lives."

To visitors Oppenheimer explains the role of the institute in the following words: "The world is passing through a period of heightened nervous tension. It is afraid of ideas, and that is perhaps inevitable in a fight for the preservation and restoration of freedom. In such a time it seems more important than ever that there should be a place where scholars from various countries may come together, learn from each other, think honestly and live in an atmosphere of genuine freedom."

The Institute of Advanced Studies has only eighteen permanent members but there are generally about a hundred guests present from all parts of the world. They are invited for several weeks or months, even for one or two years, in order to complete, in freedom from care, a work they have at heart and to enjoy the company and conversation of congenial intellects.

These conversations may develop by chance during a walk in the meadows or woods or be carried on in one of the seminars open to all, which provide occasion for stimulating debates.

But perhaps the most important debates begin at about four o'clock every afternoon in the large community room of Fuld Hall. They go by the German name of *Kaffeeklatsch*. There one may happen to find two Nobel Prize winners criticizing, from the vantage point of physics, a leading adviser of the State Department who is trying to regain his lost clarity here in the peace of Princeton; and an archaeologist who is sifting the latest excavations of the Athenian agora speculates in this connection on what remains will one day be dug up of twentieth-century culture.

That leads to the ever-recurring question of the guilt of natural science for the dilemma in which modern man finds himself. There is no lack of self-criticism. "We scholars were apostles and have become bishops," said one of the members, John Von Neumann. "We made pacts with the mighty and let ourselves be harnessed by them for their own ends. This is harmful to the pure message of science, which cares for nothing but truth."

The return to a science in search of pure truth and at the same time bound to humanism is the institute's real aspiration. Its members and friends reject—each in different words, each perhaps also for different reasons, since this is not a sect but a union of free spirits—the pretensions of applied science to call itself scientific. For in technical science, the atomic industry, biology that encroaches on nature and practical psychology that classifies, men have departed from the path of truth and allowed themselves to be made instruments of enslavement. In so far as they render aid to inhumanity they endanger the source of every real advance of the fearlessly thinking and feeling human being.

Is there any use in protesting openly against this misuse of science by power? That is a subject frequently discussed at Princeton. Certain members of the institute have come out openly with critical and warning notices, only to be misunderstood, attacked, outlawed or—worse still—made use of. An age that considers everything primarily from the viewpoint of its utility cannot resist the use even of such disinterested reports as weapons in the ideological party strife.

Consequently, in recent times things have been kept fairly quiet in the region of the Institute of Advanced Studies. But the work goes forward tranquilly.

"What are we working on?" said a member of the institute as he brought me back to the little university town of Princeton; "I suppose on the real foundations of tomorrow. All that you've seen in America in the way of technical development is not what is to come but what is already passing. It rests on the practical exploitation of basic thoughts mainly conceived and set on paper at the turn of the century. This theoretical treasury of ideas is on the decrease. New and true thoughts must be found for the practice of tomorrow. I hope that some of them may be developed by us here. And we are not, thank God, the only place in the world where creative work is being done."

"So you don't think the future will be simply an intensification of this alarming present?" I asked.

"No," he said. "In spite of everything, there is hope."